What the press says about Harlequin Romances…

"…clean, wholesome fiction…always with an upbeat, happy ending."
— *San Francisco Chronicle*

"…a work of art."
— *The Globe & Mail*, Toronto

"Nothing quite like it has happened since *Gone With the Wind…*"
— *Los Angeles Times*

"…among the top ten…"
— *International Herald-Tribune*, Paris

"Women have come to trust these clean, easy-to-read love stories about contemporary people, set in exciting foreign places."
— *Best Sellers*, New York

OTHER
Harlequin Romances
by HELEN BIANCHIN

2010—BEWILDERED HAVEN

Many of these titles are available at your local bookseller
or through the Harlequin Reader Service.

For a free catalogue listing all available Harlequin Romances,
send your name and address to:

HARLEQUIN READER SERVICE,
M.P.O. Box 707, Niagara Falls, N.Y. 14302
Canadian address: Stratford, Ontario, Canada N5A 6W4

or use order coupon at back of books.

Avenging Angel

by

HELEN BIANCHIN

Harlequin Books

TORONTO • LONDON • NEW YORK • AMSTERDAM • SYDNEY

Original hardcover edition published in 1977
by Mills & Boon Limited

ISBN 0-373-02084-8

Harlequin edition published July 1977

Printed in U.S.A.

CHAPTER ONE

TERESE brought her car to a halt and peered through the evening dusk at the numerals on the stone pillar beside the heavy wrought-iron gates guarding the entrance to the exclusive Toorak residence of Manuel Delgado—who, little did he suspect, she grimaced wryly, was about to be invaded by a veritable virago in the female form of Terese Bennett!

For the past two weeks she had endeavoured to contact him, without success. Each attempt had been smoothly met with efficient secretarial prose—'Mr Delgado is in conference and cannot be disturbed'; 'Mr Delgado is at lunch'; 'Mr Delgado is not in his office and cannot be reached'.

The thought of confronting the head of the Delgado Construction empire brought a familiar surge of anger coursing through her veins with such fervour that she didn't need to pause to gather courage or reflect on what she intended to say—the words were indelibly imprinted in her mind and needed no rehearsal!

Terese slid out from the car and crossed the footpath to inspect the gates more closely. There seemed to be no lock to bar her entry, and she found the catch and slipped it cautiously, then set out briskly along the metal-chipped driveway towards the solid double-storied mansion screened from the road by tall beech trees.

The light was fading swiftly, but even in twilight the magnificence of the Delgado residence was remarkably evident, and she stifled a gasp of admiration at her first unobstructed view. Of Mediterranean design and constructed in cream split-stone, it was impressive with its numerous archways, tiled forecourt and curved roof-tiles of deep indigo-blue.

A slight feeling of trepidation entered her limbs as she mounted the tiled steps to the front entrance, where within seconds of her pressing the doorbell the door swung open to reveal a man of middle years dressed very correctly in black. Heavens—a manservant!

'Good evening.' His voice was polite and enquiring and bore an accent.

Terese drew breath and smiled. 'I believe Mr Delgado is expecting me. If I'm early, perhaps I could step inside and wait?'

A slight frown creased the manservant's brow and she seized upon his uncertainty to step forward into the marble-tiled entrance lobby.

'Oh dear—how embarrassing! Has he not mentioned that I'm expected?' she exclaimed with every evidence of genuine perplexion.

The man appeared clearly puzzled and she caught her breath that her plan might not work after all, for possibly the arrogantly aloof Manuel Delgado was not at home and she would be shown to the door.

'Señor Delgado is dining, after which I had understood he was to attend an evening appointment. If you would care to wait I will acquaint the señor of your presence. May I have your name?'

'Bennett—Miss Terese Bennett,' Terese offered quietly.

As soon as he had withdrawn she found it impossible to stay her interested gaze from wandering over the expensive prints on the walls, and from there she cast her eyes appreciatively to the octagonal marble floor tiles of pale cream with variegated streaking grains. The lobby's focal point was the majestic curving marble staircase leading to the upper floor and totally illuminated by several ornate wall-lights at precisely-spaced intervals.

Terese pondered idly over the information she had been able to glean regarding Manuel Delgado. There had been a recent article published in one of the weekly magazines on the Spanish businessman when he had attended a society wedding. Immensely wealthy, he had emigrated from Madrid ten years ago to head the Australian branch of Delgado Construction in Melbourne. Socially sought after, he was regarded as one of the most eligible bachelors in the southern State of Victoria and his reputed success with women had earned him a rakish reputation—a characteristic which without doubt could be attributed to his paternal conquistador ancestors!

Soft footfalls seconds after the almost silent click of a door heralded the return of the manservant and one glance at his slightly harassed features confirmed that her presence was not well received.

'Señor Delgado is unable to see you, Miss Bennett,' he recited sternly.

Terese could feel her temper begin to rise and her eyes flashed angrily as she glared at the man in front of her with barely-concealed frustration. 'Whatever-your-name . . .?' she paused inquiringly.

'Santanas.'

'Santanas,' she repeated, feeling thoroughly vexed. 'You can go back from whence you came and tell the high-and-mighty Señor that I refuse to leave until I *do* see him!'

The manservant Santanas drew himself rigidly upright and squared his shoulders. 'Señor Delgado is quite emphatic . . .'

Terese's eyes snapped as she resolutely tilted her chin. 'So, Santanas, am I!'

'Miss Bennett, you would be advised not to cause trouble,' he replied coldly.

Reluctantly she smothered the unuttered words she longed to rail upon the head of this household and gave an expressive sigh. 'I have no wish to cause trouble. However, you can assure your precious Señor Delgado that I will not move from this house until——'

'Until what, young lady?' a cold hard voice questioned from behind, and Terese swiftly turned to face the man who could only be the exalted Manuel Delgado himself.

Of all she had heard describing her adversary, nothing had prepared her sufficiently to meet the chilling glint from those dark eyes nor the supreme arrogance emanating from such a rugged tautly-chiselled countenance. Tall, broad-framed and spare, he presented a formidable figure, attired as he was in black trousers and a black polo-necked jumper. Her vivid imagination added caricature horns, tail and a triple-pronged fork held in hand, and it could have been Lucifer himself standing before her.

'All right, Santanas,' he dismissed brusquely. 'I will deal with Miss Bennett.' He waited until his manservant retreated from the lobby before addressing Terese. 'You are surely aware that I find you an extremely tiresome young woman with whom I wish no contact whatever?' he queried in a steely voice, and his dark almost black eyes slowly raked her from head to toe with studied insolence, taking in the light golden glow of her skin, her vibrantly-hued auburn hair, the amber-flecked expressive brown eyes and the slim figure beneath the fashionable suede coat of light tan with its cream fur trim.

Terese clenched her fists deep within the pockets of

her coat in an attempt to control the desire to slap his hateful face. 'I could scarcely doubt it, *señor*.'

His eyes glinted dangerously. 'And now you have the audacity to force your way into my home,' he observed grimly. 'Invading my privacy, interrupting my dinner— not to mention wasting my valuable time.'

'If you had had the courtesy to acknowledge my letter or accept one of my many telephone calls I need not have invaded your home,' she retorted. 'I certainly had no wish to come here!'

He regarded her silently for several seemingly interminable minutes, during which she forced herself to hold his gaze.

'I will allow you five minutes in which to say whatever it is you consider so vitally important—then you will leave,' he evinced hardily, and swept an arm towards a door at his left.

Terese grimaced and shot him a wry glance. 'You are undoubtedly a most generous man, Señor Delgado.'

'And you, Miss Bennett, would be strongly advised not to trifle with my temper!' He flung open the door of a spacious study which at first glance appeared to be shelved floor-to-ceiling with leather-bound books.

Terese entered the room and declined a seat. She felt infinitely more secure standing on her feet and more able to do verbal battle with the hawkish hard-hearted man who moved behind the wide teak desk to stand regarding her with grim implacability.

'Well?' he demanded coldly.

There was nothing else for it but to plunge right in, she decided warily. 'There is a reason why you should not proceed with any legal action against my stepfather,' she began quietly.

'Reason?' His voice deepened noticably and became

more heavily accented as he leaned across the desk. 'There should be a reason that can exonerate a drunk behind the wheel of a car driven with such disregard that an accident occurs, and the lives of two people are extinguished?' His fingers snapped explosively in the air and she jumped involuntarily.

It wasn't difficult to summon her stepfather's kindly image to mind, she reflected pensively. How could words describe the measure of love and understanding Steve had given to a young widow and her six-year-old daughter these past seventeen years? Explain the shared laughter and happiness? The protectiveness she and Steve had developed for each other's well-being since a tragic accident had robbed them of both wife and mother less than two years ago?

Terese pulled her thoughts together with the knowledge that she would do everything she could to spare Steve anxiety—even if it meant pleading with this cynically ruthless Spaniard!

Manuel Delgado stood erect and came round the desk to sit on its edge. 'But come—this reason? It must surely be quite shattering! I am—how do you say—all ears?'

She flinched at the intended sarcasm and her eyes flashed angrily. 'You're incredibly rude and arrogant, and you have less compassion than—than—— I find you utterly despicable!'

One of his eyebrows rose slightly and he gave every indication of being undaunted by her outburst. With studied ease he extracted a slim cigarette-case from his trouser pocket, selected a thin cheroot and lit it, then exhaled the smoke with slow satisfaction.

'Miss Terese Bennett,' he drawled softly—dangerously, 'you are scarcely qualified to pass judgment.'

There was something about him that was beginning to bother her more than a little. Instinct warned that he was a man to be reckoned with, but it was more than that—much more! There was a sensual quality—a forceful vitality about him that amounted to sheer physical magnetism of a kind she hadn't previously encountered. Little wonder he had gained a rakish reputation, she mused idly. He projected an overpowering charisma that hinted alternately at ardent tenderness and passionate savagery—a man from whom any sensible girl would turn and flee!

'Steve Montgomerie was the driver of the car that killed my only brother and his son,' Manuel Delgado intoned. 'Breathalyser tests taken by the police after the accident revealed a high alcohol level which subsequent blood tests confirmed as being in excess of the legal maximum. Your stepfather is guilty of manslaughter and I intend to see he is so charged—despite any misguided pleadings on your part.'

Terese clenched her fists and her eyes gleamed with ill-concealed animosity as she suppressed the desire to hurl something at that arrogant face not too far from her own.

'His brakes failed—that was proved conclusively at the enquiry,' she cried angrily. 'I'm aware he shouldn't have attempted to drive home from his club that night, but there were extenuating circumstances that motivated him to drink as much as he did.' She hurried on before he could make scathing comment. 'Steve has been unwell for some time and the day following the accident he was to enter hospital. The tests he underwent there reveal a malignant tumour encroaching the liver—he has only a number of weeks to live.' She paused significantly and her voice was unconsciously sad. 'Surely you can see that it would be inhuman to continue with any proceedings in the circumstances?'

There was scant sympathy evident in the dark eyes of the man regarding her with intent watchfulness, and it seemed that he was deliberately weighing his words. 'Despite what you say, you are asking the impossible. It is a matter of principle.'

Terese drew herself up to her full height of five feet five inches and tilted her chin. 'I should have known you would possess no compassion,' she managed with quiet dignity. 'Mechanical failure was the cause, Señor Delgado—not drunken driving.'

The deeply etched line down each cheek lent his features a certain harshness, and she began to feel apprehensive.

'If your stepfather had ensured regular garage maintenance, the so-called "mechanical failure" would not have occurred,' he voiced coldly.

She gazed at him with frank incredulity. 'Steve had his car serviced regularly,' she asserted heatedly. 'If victimising a dying man can somehow satisfy your stuffy principles, then I feel sorry for you! And if your so-called Spanish family honour requires you to do such a thing—I can only say I'm thankful that it's not *my* family, for I wouldn't wish to claim it as such. In my code of ethics there's no honour in inhuman vengeance!'

'*Madre de Dios!* That is enough!' he exclaimed with ominous asperity, and reaching out he grasped her shoulders and mercilessly shook her until she thought her bones would snap beneath the pressure of his hands. 'Never before has anyone dared question the honour of a Delgado!' With an angry movement he thrust her away from him.

'Then it's time someone did!' Terese muttered shakily

as she met and matched the chilling anger in the depths of his eyes, and she glimpsed the tremendous effort he was making to regain control of an inimical temper.

'My brother Vicente and I,' he began bleakly, 'were the only sons of our late father, Sebastian. Vicente headed the business in Madrid where his fifteen-year-old son, Esteban—his only son—would eventually have taken over from his father.' His eyes were hard and relentless as he subjected her to a raking scrutiny. 'By your stepfather's carelessness two Delgado lives have been extinguished. As the only surviving male Delgado I am obligated to marry and provide necessary heirs.'

She couldn't help the bitter laugh that escaped her lips. 'Even on so brief an acquaintance I can't imagine any female in her right mind wanting to marry you—with or without accompanying wealth!' she flung carelessly.

There was a momentary flaring of terrible anger in the depths of those dark eyes, then his lips twisted into a mocking smile. 'Is that so? I have it in mind to make you pay for that remark. A life for a life,' he reflected sardonically. 'Steve Montgomerie's life for that of my brother—yours, Terese Bennett, for that of my brother's son.'

Terese's eyes widened in disbelief and she laughed incredulously. 'Really, Señor Delgado! Influential you may be—but you can scarcely expect to get away with it!'

His expression became entirely cynical. 'Precisely what do you expect me not to get away with?'

Angry with him for deliberately baiting her, she eyed the objects on his desk with something akin to pleasure as she mentally weighed which might inflict most pain should she need to defend herself.

'I would not advise it,' he drawled dangerously. 'Such an action would be extremely foolish.'

She flinched beneath his slow analytical appraisal and her eyes openly mirrored indignation of his studied insolence.

'For everything there is a price—will you pay it, I wonder?' he mused speculatively, and he viewed her look of horrified incredulity with a twisted smile. 'Marriage to me, the heirs I desire—in return for your stepfather's peace of mind. A question of loyalties, wouldn't you agree?'

'You must be mad!' The words burst forth without coherent thought. 'You can't possibly expect me to agree to such a—an *insane* suggestion!'

'It is hardly a suggestion—make no mistake. I have issued an ultimatum!'

'I think,' Terese almost choked with anger as she spoke, 'you are the most barbaric—*savage* I've ever encountered!' She clenched and unclenched her fists, hating him with all her heart. Marriage to such a man would be a living hell. 'But not a permanent one', a tiny voice prompted from inside her brain. Steve had at most only eight weeks to live—in all probability considerably less. Such a marriage couldn't be enforced after his death as Manuel Delgado would then have no hold over her. Surely she could survive for such a short time? It would give her immense satisfaction to be as difficult as possible in her brief role as a Delgado wife, she perceived thoughtfully. Manuel Delgado might have his revenge—but then so would she!

'Well, Miss Terese Bennett, have you reached a decision?'

'It appears I have little choice in the matter,' she indicated with slow deliberation, and kept her lashes

14

lowered with the intention of admitting defeat. ·

'You have a boy-friend—an entanglement to discard?'

She didn't—not really, unless Alan could be called an entanglement? A resident doctor at the hospital where she worked, Alan Urquhart was more friend than boy-friend—someone she could telephone and ask to partner her to a dance. His attentions were more brotherly than lover-like, and not once had his rather clumsy kisses aroused a spark of desire. Most other young men she usually gave a wide berth—to accept a date invariably involved a wrestling match at the end of the evening, and she had become heartily tired of attempting to reason that the acceptance of a date didn't mean she was prepared to indulge in sex. When it was discovered that she didn't intend to play they took off with disgust, often derisively voiced! However, there was no way she would admit to this cynical Spaniard that she was emotionally uninvolved.

'Yes, there is someone,' she declared evenly.

'Get rid of him,' he dismissed callously.

'Just like that?'

'*How* you do it is not my concern,' he shrugged impatiently. 'But do it, Terese Bennett, for by the end of the week the *Bennett* will have been legally replaced by *Delgado*.'

'How delightful!' Such succinct sarcasm—for the life of her she couldn't recall ever being so rude!

His eyes narrowed fractionally as he extracted a cigarette from a box on top of his desk and held it between his fingers. 'A word of warning, Terese Bennett,' he drawled softly. 'What I have, I hold.'

Without pausing to think she voiced with great daring —'What of *your* emotional entanglements, Señor Delgado—can you be rid of them easily in so few days? Or

15

perhaps they number too many for you to keep a count?'

'I am answerable to no woman,' he assured her silkily, and placed the cigarette between his lips.

Terese stretched out a hand as the lighter flared. 'May I?' Her tone conveyed that she thought it extremely impolite of him not to have offered her one.

'You smoke?' he queried icily.

'When it pleases me—yes.'

He pocketed the lighter with ease and regarded her steadily. 'It does not please me for you to smoke. It is a habit I abhor in women.'

Terese's eyes glittered angrily as she glared at him. 'It will just have to displease you, *señor*.'

He eyed her coldly and she saw that his lips were set in an ominous line. 'I sincerely hope you do not intend to continue displaying such defiance. As my wife you will be called upon to play an active social role, and it is essential there is a semblance of harmony between us —at least in the presence of others. You will find I shall insist upon it,' he finished implacably.

'You can insist all you like,' she assured him with spirit. 'I refuse to become subservient—blindly obedient to every word uttered by a tyrannical husband.'

'Then I shall warn you *once* that my patience has its limitations,' he advised bleakly. 'If you insist on behaving like a child, you will be treated as one.'

'Oh? I wouldn't find that difficult to believe. Your secretary gave the impression of being remarkably servile. Do you keep a ruler in your drawer to rap her knuckles every once in a while?'

For a moment she thought she had provoked him too far, and she watched in fearful fascination as he moved slowly round the desk to sit in the high-backed leather-upholstered chair. With admirable control he crushed

16

the butt of his cigarette into an ashtray and drew forward a notepad and pen.

'I shall need some particulars in order to obtain a special licence. You will give me your name in full and date of birth.'

Very businesslike, Terese perceived wryly as she imparted the necessary information.

'You realise I will defer dropping all charges against your stepfather until after the marriage? You will also give me the name of his doctor.'

A worried frown creased her forehead. 'What am I to tell Steve?'

'I'm sure you'll think of something,' Manuel Delgado said with intended sarcasm. 'You haven't lacked in determination to save his soul. I fail to see so minor a detail deterring you.'

Terese swept her gaze to the man opposite, dislike and animosity evident in every line of her features. 'You are the most arrogantly insolent man I've ever had the misfortune to meet!' she sallied resentfully.

'And you, Terese Bennett, have taken too many liberties with both my patience and my temper.' He rose to his feet and moved towards the door with lithe ease. 'Santanas will see you out.'

She looked at him uncertainly and a hesitant frown formed fleetingly.

'You will be contacted when the necessary arrangements have been made. *Adios.*' His voice was calculatingly cold, his expression grim and forbidding, and Terese felt the stirrings of unease begin as his manservant appeared and stood silently waiting.

With not so much as a flicker of an eyelid Santanas escorted her to the front entrance and the door closed with a dull metallic click seconds afterwards.

Darkness had fallen to shroud the grounds with an inky blackness, and Terese turned up the collar of her coat and thrust her hands deep into the pockets in an attempt to shut out some of the bitterly cold wind. July in Melbourne was notably wet cold and invariably windy, and this evening was no exception. She stepped down on to the driveway and had actually covered a few yards when several lamps lining the driveway to the gates were switched on and threw a welcome illuminating glow.

Only when she had driven several miles did she manage to dispel much of the all-encompassing air of foreboding that her confrontation with Manuel Delgado had aroused. Of one thing she was certain—Steve must not guess just how great a sacrifice she was making on his behalf. Somehow she had to convince him she had been swept off her feet by the Spanish construction engineer —a lie she hated to have to enact, for she was essentially honest and not given to fabrication. Could she possibly hope that Steve would believe she could throw caution to the wind and marry a man she had known for less than a week? He was far too astute not to guess the truth—even if she implied that she had previously made the Spaniard's acquaintance. And there was the hospital —she was due to begin night duty tomorrow. At the best of times Matron was inclined to be a bit of a dragon, and giving one or two days' notice of her intention to leave was bound to raise wrathful comment.

Why, oh, *why* couldn't there be a few weeks' engagement to give her time to sort everything out satisfactorily before the wedding instead of only a few days?

CHAPTER TWO

Terese married Manuel Delgado at a register office three days later in a starkly simple ceremony that seemed far removed from any bondage she had fondly imagined her wedding vows would take.

'Oh, sweet dreams of yesteryear,' she echoed silently as she stood at his side, unable to move, as if he held her prisoner.

She had chosen to wear a long crushed-velvet skirt of dull blue with a matching body-shirt and jumper, unaware that the colour accented the honey-creaminess of her skin and heightened her vibrantly-hued hair. How different she would have wished this day to be, with herself dressed in white flowing silk and a misty veil, a bouquet of rich cream roses held in hand, and a feeling of joy when her husband slipped on to her finger a ring of gold.

Reality swept away the misty dreams as she sat opposite him in the vast formal dining-room of his home. Steve had been present at the register office as one of the witnesses, on that Terese had been adamant, but he had diplomatically declined her invitation to dinner afterwards at the Delgado residence. Not that she could entirely blame him, for if she had had a choice she would opt out of it herself!

It was hardly a convivial evening, and with dinner comprising no fewer than eight courses the meal seemed interminably long. Terese stifled a slightly hysterical desire to laugh. All this was a mockery—the food, the champagne, the solicitous attention of Santanas' wife, Sofia.

'The food is not to your liking?'

Terese looked at her husband carefully. 'I'm not very hungry.'

'Some more wine?'

She shook her head and wondered if she was foolish to refuse. To pass the remainder of the evening in an alcoholic haze might not be a bad idea. A few short hours ago she had been wed, and as inevitably as night follows day Manuel Delgado would soon take her to his bed. It was there in his eyes, the slightly cynical set of his mouth.

The past few days had been a nightmare of which convincing Steve had been the most difficult. Her notice at the Royal Children's Hospital evoked severe disapproval from Matron and had invited a lecture on the merits of persuing a worthwhile career instead of favouring marriage, which that good lady considered could be forsaken. There had been last-minute shopping to do, the added disadvantage of being on night duty, so that consequently she now felt completely enervated.

'*Gracias*, Sofia. We will have coffee in the lounge.'

Terese cast Sofia an apologetic smile at the sound of Manuel's voice, and the smile was reciprocated. It was obvious Sofia labelled her as a nervous bride whose lack of appetite was understandable.

'Some *coñac* in your coffee?'

Terese shook her head as she took the cup and saucer from his hand. 'No—thank you,' she added reluctantly.

His eyebrows quirked a little as he stood regarding her enigmatically. 'You are remarkably docile this evening.'

She raised her eyes to his. 'I'm tired.'

'An attempt to beget my sympathy?'

'That would prove fruitless, wouldn't it, *señor*?' she

20

voiced bitterly. 'I'm regarded as a form of revenge and my feelings are therefore expendable.'

'You would be advised to accept the reality of the situation,' he drawled somewhat dryly.

'I shall hate every minute of it,' she declared broodingly.

His eyebrows rose a fraction and his features assumed an entirely cynical expression. 'Indeed? You surprise me. I had associated neither naïveté nor stupidity among your attributes, and,' he paused imperceptibly, 'my name is Manuel, as you are fully aware. Isabella will think it strange for her newly-acquired aunt to address her beloved Tio so formally.'

She blinked tiredly and gazed at him clearly puzzled. 'Isabella? Tio?'

'My niece Isabella. The daughter and only surviving member of my brother Vicente's family,' he explained with precise care. 'My goddaughter, and until she reaches the age of twenty-five she remains under my legal guardianship.'

Unable to prevent the quiver in her voice, she stammered curiously, 'How—how old is she?'

'Eight years.'

'I see,' she murmured indistinctly.

'I doubt that you do,' Manuel corrected dryly. 'She is a quiet, obedient child. I wish to keep it that way.'

Terese flashed him a perceptive glance and her eyes were frankly indignant. 'Are you implying that if *I* question your authority, your niece will also?'

'Will you deny that you do not intend presenting an example of docility?' he parried imperturbably.

'Surely the behaviour of an adult cannot be compared with the intended disciplining of a child? I am entirely independent, and most certainly not answerable to you!'

21

He took time to light a thin cheroot and expelled the smoke slowly. 'Legally you gave up your independence some hours ago, and most assuredly you are answerable to me. I must insist you follow my direction, and any grievances you may have will not be aired in company. As to household matters—Santanas enjoys the dual role of manservant and chauffeur, his wife Sofia attends to the meals, and their daughter Maria does the cleaning. Should you wish to go shopping in the city, or elsewhere, at any time, Santanas will drive you in the Daimler.'

Terese had held her tongue with admirable restraint, but now she gave way with little pretence to patience. 'You appear to have thought of everything except what I am to do with my time. I'm a working girl, not a favoured daughter of the idle rich, and I refuse to sit and twiddle my thumbs all day in this great mansion!'

'You are sadly mistaken if you imagine I will tolerate your rebellion,' Manuel evinced hardily.

'You're incredibly chauvinistic,' she retorted.

'Is that a disadvantage?' he queried silkily.

'You resemble a feudal lord, no less!' She glared at him and her eyes flashed indignantly. 'Tell me, must I curtsey in your presence and not speak until spoken to?'

His eyes narrowed fractionally, and as the seconds crept by there was an element of danger in his silence as if he was controlling his temper with difficulty.

The seconds became minutes that increased the tension between them until she could bear it no longer. Tiredly she stood to her feet.

'If you have no objection, I'd like to go to my room.'

'*Our* room—need I remind you?' Manuel drawled sardonically as he negligently leaned one arm along the mantel above the wide fireplace. His expression was far from indolent. Terese observed and he reminded her of a panther at watch over its prey, content that all avenues of escape were impregnable—the kill a foregone conclusion.

'Since this farcical marriage was arranged solely for the purpose of furthering the Delgado lineage, I would be extremely dense to foster the notion that I might sleep alone,' she snapped crossly.

His eyes darkened ominously as he pressed the remains of his cheroot into a nearby ashtray, and with cool deliberation he shortened the distance between them.

Terese gasped as hard hands closed over her arms and she had no time to utter any protest before his mouth descended, and the lips that parted hers were hard and merciless with intent to punish.

Her struggles were ineffectual as his hand slid through her hair to hold fast her head, and she uttered an almost silent moan of pain as his fingers heedlessly pulled against the tender roots. It seemed unending—the relentless pressure of his mouth, his caressing hands deliberately seeking her response.

When at last he lifted his head she uttered a shuddering gasp and veiled her eyes with tear-wet lashes so that he couldn't glimpse the hurt and humiliation hidden in their depths. She had been kissed before, but never with quite such a measure of leashed violence. She felt limp and emotionless, and when he impatiently swept her up into his arms she was incapable of offering resistance.

He carried her as effortlessly as if she weighed scarcely more than a child, and she experienced a feeling of unreality as he ascended the gently-curving staircase and purposefully strode to a suite of rooms at the far end of a corridor.

The bedroom was incredibly large, and Terese's nervous gaze flicked straight to the bed which at first glance seemed to dominate the room. Momentarily she closed her eyes in the hope that when she opened them again she would discover it was all a bad dream. With no pretence to gentleness she was dropped down on to the brocade counterpane.

'I will not answer for the consequences if you continue to arouse my temper,' Manuel warned bleakly.

Terese felt the stirrings of fear begin to knot painfully in the pit of her stomach. Summoning as much dignity as she could muster, she slid off the far side of the bed and stood regarding him across its width.

'There's no need for you to threaten me with—with force,' she voiced warily. The hard strength of his hands on her flesh still ached, and unconsciously she rubbed her arms in an attempt to ease the painful bruising. Her mouth felt numb, and more than anything she wanted to slip between the covers on that comfortable-looking bed and go to sleep. She was so tired and emotionally wrung-out that she was almost swaying on her feet.

'The word you seem hesitant to use is rape,' he corrected wryly as he casually slipped his suit jacket from his shoulders and loosened his tie.

She watched in mesmerised fascination as he unbuttoned his silk shirt and cast it over the arm of a velvet button-backed chair, and she blushed brilliantly when he met her gaze. He smiled sardonically and sat down on the edge of the bed and bent to remove his shoes and socks. As he stood and began unfastening his trousers she spluttered into speech.

'My clothes—I don't know where they are,' she said jerkily, and fixed her attention on her hand where the wide gold band of the third finger of her left hand brought into focus that she was now a chattel of one

Manuel Delgado—for better or worse. And it would be for worse, of that she was sure!

'Relax,' Manuel said bluntly. 'I am a man—like any other.'

Maybe, Terese fought desperately to retain a vestige of calm, but there had been no men in her life—at least not in that sense.

'The bathroom—I—I'd like a shower. And my clothes —please tell me where they are,' she pleaded quickly.

There was fleeting curiosity in the dark glance he flicked in her direction. 'The door behind you,' he enlightened her, 'leads to a dressing-room where Sofia has no doubt had Maria unpack your clothes. Beyond the dressing-room is a bathroom.'

She thanked him briefly and fled, closing the door quickly behind her. There was no lock, no bolt to ensure uninterrupted privacy, and she wasted little time over her ablutions. The fear that he might walk in indicated the speed by which she hurriedly showered and slipped into cream silk pyjamas. From habit she brushed her hair with long vigorous strokes and began braiding it as she moved into the dressing-room. Her underwear had been carefully placed in drawers and her clothes hung behind the sliding doors of a huge closet. There was no sign of any masculine toiletries or clothing, and she concluded that Manuel must possess a similar suite.

Her stomach was behaving strangely and her heart beat a crazy thunderous tattoo as she re-entered the bedroom. With a sense of fatalism she took one step after the other towards the centre of the room, to halt nervously a few feet away from the edge of that great bed. She cast him a surreptitious glance from beneath long dark-fringed lashes and found to her chagrin that he was regarding her with cynical appraisal. She would not, she determined stoically, she simply would *not* let him see that she was nervous.

'Childishly braided hair and enveloping nightwear hardly precipitate my beneficence,' Manuel drawled dangerously as he moved towards her. 'You look poised for flight—but there can be no escape, can there?' With only a short towel wound about his hips he looked incredibly fit and virile. A small medallion on a slim gold chain about his neck nestled among a mat of dark curling hair, thus making it impossible to detect his choice of patron saint.

'I braid my hair at night to prevent it tangling,' Terese said evenly. A lump suddenly rose in her throat and she swallowed painfully. Oh, dear heaven, if only it were tomorrow and all this was behind her!

He reached out and began to unfasten her hair. 'Compliance?' he queried with a sardonic twist of his lips.

Terese closed her eyes as he drew her into his arms, and her hands clenched against her thighs as she felt his lips seek the golden-smooth skin in the delicate hollows at the base of her throat. His hands moved with a calculated sensual expertise, and she froze when his fingers began unfastening the buttons of her pyjama jacket. Too late she tried to close the gaping edges, only to have the restricting garment wrenched firmly down over her arms, and her eyes sparked furiously alive as his hands went to her waist.

'No!' The sound left her lips as an anguished gasp, and she began to struggle with every ounce of physical strength she possessed.

With very little effort he forced her hands together behind her back, and, flushed from her exertions, she sank her teeth into his shoulder and heard his sharply-drawn breath with satisfaction.

'You are behaving like an hysterical virgin,' Manuel rasped grimly as he spread a hand around her throat and raised her chin with his thumb. His eyes were dark and angry. 'You were agreeable to this marriage and all it entails—so what game are you playing, little cat?'

Terese just looked at him, and of its own volition her lower lip began to tremble and tears sprang to her eyes. 'Go to hell, Manuel Delgado,' she whispered shakily.

He swore briefly, explicitly, in Spanish. '*Madre mia*, you almost tempt me,' he growled as he shook her none too gently. His mouth ravaged hers, demanding a response as he urged her outraged senses, throbbing into awareness, before claiming her with a mastery that destroyed all of her preconceived illusions.

A wide shaft of daylight filtered across the room and she roused sleepily at the soft swishing sound of drapes being drawn.

'I have brought you some coffee and freshly-baked rolls, *señora*.'

Terese blinked slowly and reality dawned as she recognised Sofia's comfortably-proportioned figure bending over her.

'Shall I run your bath?' Sofia asked matter-of-factly as she poured steaming aromatic liquid into a cup and added sugar and cream. 'The Señor will return soon with the little one—he left early after breakfast to collect her from the convent. They were to do some shopping, I believe.'

'Thank you,' Terese acknowledged with a slight smile.

'Lunch is served in the family dining-room at one o'clock, *señora*,' Sofia said quietly as she returned from the bathroom and gave a satisfied nod as Terese glanced quickly at her watch, surprise that it was so late evident on her expressive features.

Midday already! It didn't seem possible! She bit into a warm crisp roll with enjoyment and quickly finished it and the coffee before sliding out from the covers. The bath was filled with hot water to which she added a liberal quantity of delicately-scented essence, noting with interest the luxurious appointments evident from the mosaic tiles and ornamental tap fittings to the mirrors reaching floor to ceiling along two walls. It was possible to view one's nudity with startling clarity, she perceived wryly as she quickly stepped into the oval bathtub.

She soaked unrepentantly for as long as she dared, brooding ruminatively as waves of shame and self-disgust flowed over her at the memory of the passion Manuel had aroused only hours before. Intent on contemplative thought, she didn't immediately notice the door swing open, and her startled gasp of outrage was very real as she looked up at the sound of her husband's voice.

'Do you usually conduct your bathing with such dedication?' he queried sardonically, and reached for a towel, giving every indication of enveloping her slender form within its folds just as soon as she stepped out.

'What do you think you're doing?' she asked in tones bordering on slight hysteria.

'What does it look like?' There was cynical amusement lurking in the depths of his eyes. 'Come, you will be late for lunch if you do not hurry,' he bade decisively, and leant forward to tug the linked chain holding the bath-plug. In a few short seconds almost all of the water

28

had gurgled away, to leave her sparsely covered in soap bubbles.

Terese eyed him with ill-concealed chagrin. 'I hate you, Manuel Delgado!' she snapped angrily as he effortlessly lifted her out and deposited her in front of him. Her embarrassment was vividly real and she felt a tide of telling colour flood her cheeks.

'So you do, *querida*,' he allowed mockingly as he draped the towel around her and released the gaily-patterned bath-cap from her head so that her hair tumbled down about her shoulders. He regarded her silently for several long minutes before querying indulgently, 'Was it so very hateful, little cat?'

'Yes—utterly!' Terese declared vehemently, knowing he referred to his lovemaking. 'I have bruises everywhere.'

'Poor *niña*,' Manuel drawled unsympathetically.

'You are an uncaring, insensitive brute!' she flung at him carelessly, and took a backward step as he leant forward and caught her chin between lean hard fingers.

'I scarcely expected a chaste inexperienced girl beneath my hands,' he offered wryly, and his eyes were dark and unfathomable. 'Be assured I could have been far less gentle.'

Terese could gather little from his inscrutable expression. 'I'd like to get dry and then dress,' she said warily.

'Of course,' he agreed with a slight smile, and released her chin.

Alone and free from his somewhat disturbing presence, she hurriedly completed her toilette and selected a long skirt of fine lightweight wool in a deep shade of tan from the closet and topped it with a cream shirt. Her hair she quickly wound into a knot at her nape

29

before applying the minimum of make-up. There, that should do—at least she felt reasonably poised and more than ready to match her husband's sardonic brand of sarcasm.

Quite what she expected to find when she re-entered the bedroom she was unsure, but to discover Manuel waiting to escort her downstairs to lunch was something of a surprise.

'You imagined I would display a discourtesy and allow you to find your own way to a room the whereabouts of which you are unfamiliar with?' He seemed vaguely displeased when she nodded, and his eyes darkened when she endeavoured to move her arm away from his grasp as they left the room.

'I am no hypocrite,' she voiced quietly. 'I can't pretend affection when there is only dislike between us.'

'Downstairs,' Manuel began in a carefully controlled voice as he gripped her arm in an ungentle grasp, 'waits a young child who now regards me as both uncle and father. I will go to any lengths to protect her from further unhappiness. If you by word or action give her the impression that our relationship is other than harmonious I will personally ensure that you regret it. Do you understand?'

Terese met his implacable compelling features and stifled a gasp as his grip on her arm tightened. 'I hope you don't intend me to be openly affectionate,' she glared at him eloquently. 'To gaze at you with adoring eyes would be more than I could tolerably manage!'

'*Por Dios!*' he exclaimed harshly. 'Take care, foolish wife, that you do not unleash my temper—I can promise it will be far from pleasant.'

She stared at him angrily and wished with all her

heart that she could walk out of this house and never return.

As they made their way along the corridor to the head of the stairs it took every ounce of effort to force a smile to her lips and reconcile herself to the casually-placed arm about her waist. Silently she moved down the stairs at his side and stepped across the marble-tiled floor where beyond a wide archway he led her to a comfortably-furnished room. It lacked the size and splendour of the formal dining-room, but it exuded a cosiness and informality which was strangely comforting.

Almost as soon as Manuel closed the door behind them a small figure detached herself from a settee at the far end of the room and took a few hesitant steps towards them.

'Come, Isabella,' Manuel beckoned gently. 'I want you to meet Terese.' His smile was warm and it softened his sternly-lined features miraculously.

Terese successfully hid her astonishment as the slightly-built child ran to the man at her side to be swept high into his arms.

'Hey, *pequeña*,' he chided gently as Isabella hid her face against his neck. 'I do believe you are almost as shy of your new aunt as she is of you. *Si*,' he elaborated with a soft chuckle, and added persuasively, 'Why don't you look and see for yourself?'

Slowly the little girl lifted her head and turned slightly to view Terese, regarding her solemnly for all of sixty seconds before dissolving into delicious giggles at the outrageously cheeky wink from Terese's dancing eyes.

What a delightful child! Such beautiful dark eyes in a wistful, delicately-boned face.

At that moment Sofia entered the dining-room

through a swing-door from the kitchen and deposited a tureen of thick vegetable soup in the centre of the table.

'Are we really to see the kangaroos today, Tio Manuel?'

'But of course, *meniña*. Did I not promise that we would? Just as soon as we have partaken of Sofia's excellent soup and the tortilla. *Si?*'

'*Si*, Tio Manuel,' Isabella agreed with a measure of excitement.

He slipped out a chair and lowered his niece into it, then moved around the table to hold out a chair for Terese and let his hands rest momentarily on her shoulders before he took his place at the head of the table.

Terese ate well, enjoying the tasty soup followed by a delicious omelette with cheese and crusty bread. She left most of the conversation to Manuel as she thought it prudent not to overwhelm Isabella with meaningless chatter.

Despite her antipathy towards Manuel she had to concede that he knew exactly how to handle his niece— moreover, the affection between uncle and niece was quite touching. His patience and gently-teasing manner with the little girl was something Terese found difficult to reconcile with the hard ruthlessness of the man. She suppressed a slight shiver in the knowledge that as an enemy Manuel Delgado was infinitely formidable.

Directly after lunch and well wrapped against the cold, they drove out on to the Maroondah Highway en route to the Sir Colin MacKenzie Sanctuary at Healesville, where Isabella displayed an avid interest in the birds and animals. Her natural curiosity was endearing and Manuel tirelessly recited given information at his niece's request, lifting her shoulder-high on numerous occasions to obtain a better view. However, it was the kangaroos that won the day—hopping curiously towards them to accept titbits of food. Isabella was timid at first of the engagingly tame marsupials, but when she saw how gracefully they took food from Terese's hand she needed little encouragement to follow Terese's example and her enchanted chuckles drew smiles from several onlookers.

Terese felt the afternoon had a strange feeling of unreality. She couldn't help smiling at Isabella on several occasions, and more than once drew an oddly attentive glance from Manuel as she laughed spontaneously over the antics of a koala bear on the branch of a gum-tree— but there was no spontaneity in her manner towards her husband. Whenever he sought to draw her into conversation she would smile and answer as briefly as possible.

It was almost five o'clock when they left the Sanctuary, and the picnic hamper thoughtfully provided by Sofia revealed a flask of hot coffee together with a small flask of hot chocolate for Isabella, some delicious sandwiches and thick wedges of fruit cake. Terese supervised the pouring and passing out of liquid refreshment and couldn't resist a tiny reflective smile as she remembered similar picnic hampers shared with Steve and her mother on countless occasions during her childhood— although their mode of transport had never been as ultimately luxurious as the Mercedes-Benz sports saloon that Manuel Delgado had chosen to use today.

Isabella drooped visibly after the first few miles of the journey home, and Terese responded readily to the child's rather sleepy request to sit on her lap.

'I think I like you, Terese,' Isabella proclaimed as she laid her head against Terese's shoulder.

Terese smiled and felt her arms tighten of their own

33

volition about the slight little scrap. 'I think I like you, too, poppet.'

'What is a "poppet", please, Terese?'

'An affectionate nickname for a delightful child.'

'Is it really?' Isabella questioned sleepily.

'Really,' Terese answered gently.

The remainder of the drive was achieved in silence, and the light misty drizzle outside developed into heavy rain, which together with the dusk of evening made visibility difficult. A cassette-recorder emitted soothingly-muted music and Terese watched the wet bitumen in idle fascination between each swish of the windscreen wipers.

At the Delgado residence—Terese couldn't for the life of her call it *home*—Isabella was whisked upstairs by the capable Maria for a bath before dinner, but only after Isabella had extracted Terese's promise to read a bedtime story before being tucked in for the night.

'The child appears to like you.'

Terese looked up from brushing her hair and met the dark sardonic gaze of her husband as he moved towards her from his dressing-room. He was freshly shaven and had changed his clothes in favour of dark trousers and a navy body-shirt which he had left unbuttoned at the neck. His presence set the nerves tingling along her spine and she tensed at the overpowering masculinity of the man. Thoroughly cross with herself, she stroked the brush vigorously through the length of her hair, then deftly twisted it into a simple knot on top of her head and pushed in a few pins to hold it in place.

'Do you find that so strange?' Terese returned her attention to the mirror in front of her and began to apply make-up with care. She too, had changed, favouring a long dress of pale dull-green wool-jersey with soft revers turned back over a scooped neckline and long sleeves gathered into a wide buttoned cuff at each wrist.

'I was not aware that I implied it so,' Manuel drawled wryly as he moved to stand behind her, and reaching out he released her hair. 'Your hair is beautiful, *querida*. You will refrain from twisting it into that unbecoming knot.'

Terese bristled at his air of possessiveness and her eyes flashed indignantly at his reflection in the mirror. 'I shall wear my hair any way I choose,' she declared firmly, and quickly began to re-wind its length.

'You will do as I say,' he commanded dangerously, and caught her hands in an iron grip.

'You're hurting me!' she protested as she tried unsuccessfully to pull her hands free.

With an angry movement he let them go, and grasping her by the arms he pulled her to her feet and swung her round to face him. 'You are by far the most aggravating female I have ever encountered,' he bit out reprovingly, and his eyes gleamed darkly as they raked her stormy features.

She ran the edge of her tongue nervously along her lower lip and unconsciously clenched her teeth against the agonizing strength of his hands. She stared up at him wordlessly for several long minutes and gave a slight involuntary shudder as he drew her close against him and fastened his mouth on hers with an ungentle intensity. Her eyes filled with tears that spilled over and ran slowly down her cheeks, and it didn't help at all when he lifted his head to inspect her ravaged face with grim implacability. The second button from his shirt-collar was eye-level and she resolutely gave it her undivided attention as she willed the tears to cease. His hand beneath her chin drew an inarticulate sound from her throat. She wouldn't meet his cynical gaze—she simply wouldn't!

'I did warn you that to rouse my temper could prove unpleasant?'

'So you did, Manuel Delgado,' Terese managed shakily as he released her. Vexedly she brushed the back of her hand across first one damp cheek and then the other.

'Go and bathe your face,' he ordered brusquely. 'Isabella is waiting for us to bid her goodnight.'

She escaped through to the bathroom and once there sponged her face repeatedly with cold water. There was little she could do to hide the inflamed swollen appearance of her eyes, but with freshly-applied make-up and the skilful use of eye-shadow and eye-liner the overall effect was not too bad.

Manuel subjected her to a searching scrutiny when she re-entered the bedroom and she quickly veiled her eyes as he lifted her chin. Apparently satisfied with the result, he released her, and turning towards the door she was forced to suffer his clasp on her elbow as they walked together down the corridor to Isabella's room.

Their arrival brought an ecstatic greeting from the deliciously-scented bundle in pink rosebud-sprigged pyjamas who promptly hopped back into a bed that had no fewer than three beautifully-dressed dolls and a teddy-bear seated on the counterpane.

'I see I'm to have an audience,' Terese teased gently as she admired the daintily feminine room. The colour theme was rose-pink and had obviously been decorated especially for Isabella's needs.

'You don't mind if they listen too?' Isabella sought anxiously of Terese, and for a moment her bright eyes seemed to cloud as if she was schooling herself to accept a refusal.

Terese temporarily forgot Manuel's presence as she

sat down on the quilted bed. 'Why should I mind?' she began gently. 'To banish them to the other side of the room would hurt their feelings. Do they like animal stories?'

'Oh, yes,' Isabella moved excitedly as she pointed to each of the dolls in turn. 'Sasha loves horses, Miska adores dogs, but Suki doesn't have any special likes—except maybe kittens.'

'Did you discover beautiful names all by yourself?'

'My *abuela*—my grandmother—she helped me,' Isabella offered informatively, then wriggled with delight as Manuel clicked his teeth and shook his head from side to side. 'I think Tio Manuel wants you to get on with the story, Terese. Perhaps you better had,' she advised impishly, 'otherwise he might not take us to the snow-fields tomorrow.'

Terese hid a wry smile, although she sensed that Manuel intended the gesture to be in the nature of a teasing reminder—Tio Manuel could apparently do no wrong and was God, the Saints and Father Christmas all rolled into one, she preceived from Isabella's expression of adoration.

'Hmmn,' she voiced tolerantly, and tilted her head to one side. 'I think it's much more likely Tio Manuel is afraid of Sofia's frowns if we are late down to dinner.'

There was a peal of unsuppressed laughter that subsided into hand-stifled giggles from Isabella at this suggestion, and there was pride in her voice as she declared that Tio Manuel was afraid of nothing and nobody. Terese didn't doubt it was true for a moment!

It seemed strange to sit down to dinner at eight o'clock in the evening, and even more disturbing to be seated opposite the dark cynical Spaniard whose very expression dared her to do other than present the appearance of a fond newly-wed wife. Very well, for the sake of the servants she would try not to raise her voice in argument against him—but she wasn't making any promises!

Sofia's proficiency in the kitchen was of *cordon bleu* standard, and Terese savoured each course with an enjoyment that was genuine, pleased that her compliment of the food at the end of the meal brought forth a smiling response.

Conversation during dinner was desultory—in fact it was downright sparse. In between the consommé and an entrée of scallops Manuel confirmed his intention to drive to the snowfields at Mount Buller the following day. Jolly good, Terese silently enthused—perhaps she could aim a few snowballs in his direction all in the guise of fun. The *paella* was eaten in total silence, and after the escalopes of veal Labrador she felt obliged to praise the wine.

To this Manuel lifted his glass in salute and uttered something in Spanish, the meaning of which obviously escaped her. '"*Uvas con queso saben a beso*"—grapes and cheese taste like a kiss,' he repeated, and translated mockingly. 'You compliment my choice of wine, *mi mujer*—am I to understand you compliment my kisses also?'

'No!' she denied emphatically in a low undertone, and deliberately refrained from finishing the wine in her glass.

Sofia served their coffee in the *sala* at Manuel's direction. It was a charming room—large and elegantly furnished it held a warmth and informality Terese found very much to her liking. She longed to be able to explore Manuel Delgado's spacious home, preferably alone, for

38

without his unsettling presence she could wander at will.

'*Gracias*, Sofia. That will be all. *Buenas noches*,' he dismissed quietly, and when the door had closed behind Sofia's amply-rounded figure he sought the warmth of the log fire burning in the large grate. He looked infinitely masculine standing there with an arm resting on the marble mantel, and the flickering light of the fire cast strange shadows down the planes of his face.

'How do you like your coffee?' Terese asked civilly as she poured her own from the stainless steel pot.

'At this time of night—black with a dash of *coñac* and two lumps of sugar,' he advised dryly, taking it from her as she silently handed him the cup and saucer.

She sipped the contents of her cup with every evidence of calm, whereas inwardly she was close to screaming out at him in temper. He could at least make polite conversation instead of subjecting her to this silent analytical appraisal!

'You would do well to veil your eyes—they reveal your thoughts rather more clearly than you might realise,' he drawled sardonically, and his voice seemed to deepen and acquire a distinct accent.

'We're alone,' she flashed indignantly. 'You can hardly expect me to smile disarmingly.'

'Yet you enjoyed our outing this afternoon, did you not?' he questioned enigmatically.

She replaced her cup down on to the coffee table and sat back slowly. 'Isabella is an engaging child.'

'Yes,' he agreed seriously. 'Her welfare means much to me.'

Terese fingered her hair as she regarded him circumspectly. There was something devilishly dangerous about this man—a quality some women would find attractive, for he possessed an undoubted magnetism.

'She speaks English very well,' she commented with genuine interest, in the hope of discovering more about the child.

'Vicente employed a tutor to teach the children fluent English and French, as well as assisting with their native Spanish, of course,' Manuel remarked informatively.

'Of course,' Terese echoed silently. Heaven forbid! 'Are you also fluent in French?' she queried aloud in an attempt at politeness.

'I am fluent in five languages,' he answered cursorily, and there was no pride in his voice—it was a simple statement of fact. 'Isabella attends a convent, from which I collect her each Saturday morning at nine,' he continued. 'She spends the weekends at home and returns to school on Sunday evening. It is an arrangement which has proved entirely satisfactory during the six months she has been in my care.'

Terese looked at him in astonishment. 'Surely she would feel secure attending as a day pupil,' she said incredulously, and would have continued had Manuel not smoothly interjected.

'I do not agree. This was discussed when Vicente wished to assign the child into my care for two years. As a boarder she is in the company of other girls of a similar age, and after-class activities are organised under supervision.'

'I daresay,' she agreed pensively. 'But for a child so young I think she'd be happier in her home environment after school each day.'

'Really? With only Sofia and Maria for company—both of whom are busily occupied at such times? I am

40

rarely home before six each evening—a mere hour before her bedtime,' he concluded coldly, and there was an ominous glint of anger lurking in the depths of his eyes as he moved away from the fireplace. 'I will not have you question my authority where Isabella is concerned.'

Terese stood to her feet with the light of battle gleaming in her amber-flecked brown eyes. The man was impossibly overbearing! 'Am I to be subjected to such authority—like a child?' She glared at him angrily. 'Perhaps now would be as good a time as any for me to tell you that I am going to see Steve each day. It won't be long before he'll have to go into hospital, and until then I intend spending as much time with him as I possibly can.'

'And if I forbid it?' he questioned silkily.

'I'll go just the same,' she vowed with determination.

They stood facing each other like proud animals, one displaying the lithe strength of a panther, the other the fluid grace of a gazelle. That should they do battle the victory of one over the other was a foregone conclusion didn't enter Terese's head for a moment.

'I shall instruct Santanas to take you,' Manuel allowed brusquely after a seemingly interminable length of time. 'I insist you restrict your visits to weekdays, and you will return here by four o'clock each afternoon. Is that clearly understood?'

Terese was wholly aware of his barely-leashed anger, and yet she couldn't refrain from commenting sarcastically. 'Your consideration is overwhelming! I don't need the use of your car or your chauffeur—I'd much prefer to take a tram!'

'Santanas will take you, or you will not go at all!'

She flinched as he caught hold of her shoulders and

41

for a moment she thought he meant to shake the life from her.

'Be warned, Terese,' he heeded. 'I intend you to obey me.'

'Oh, go to hell, Manuel Delgado!' she cried defiantly.

'*Madre de Dios!*' he exclaimed savagely. 'Never before have I had to deal with such a spitfire! Perhaps you will understand *this.*'

She struggled the instant his meaning became clear, but by then she was experiencing the indignity of being held face-down across his powerful thighs. The stinging slaps he administered to her scantily-clad posterior were numerous and hurt abominably long after he stood her to her feet.

In silence Terese raised stormy eyes to his ruthless features and she felt perilously close to bursting into tears. Apart from an incredulously-voiced 'ouch!' when he dealt the first slap she hadn't cried out once. Now all she wanted to do was to get far away from this tyrannical man before he had the satisfaction of seeing her in tears for the second time in less than three hours.

'If you'll excuse me, I'll go to bed,' she said shakily, and without waiting for him to comment she turned and left the *sala* to hurry up the stairs as if the devil himself were at her heels.

With the bedroom door safely shut behind her, Terese shed her clothes, showered and donned pyjamas with a speed that bordered on panic, and only when she slipped between the bedcovers did she give way to tears.

'I'll leave—I don't care!' she silently vowed again and again until she became exhausted and fell into an uneasy sleep.

She had no idea how long it was before Manuel entered the room, but somehow she sensed his presence and her heart began to thud against her ribs. She forced herself to breathe evenly and uttered a silent prayer that he would not switch on the light, for if he did he would surely see she was shamming. It seemed an age before she felt the other side of the bed depress with the weight of his body and her muscles involuntarily tensed. She determined vengefully that if he touched her she would fight him with every ounce of energy she possessed! So consumed was she with fury against him that it was almost disappointing when it became apparent he had lapsed into a deep and seemingly relaxed sleep.

Oh! she silently seethed. How she longed to turn and rail her fists against his hateful frame. She'd make him pay if it was the last thing she did, and it was during her various schemings as to how she could accomplish this that she finally fell asleep.

CHAPTER THREE

Isabella presented an adorable figure dressed in bright red ski-wear after breakfast next morning, and she chattered practically non-stop all the way to Mount Buller.

Terese was able to discern a few facts that were somewhat surprising, for it was becoming apparent the child had accepted the death of her father and brother with a matter-of-factness that was slightly disquieting—almost as if neither had played a very important or emotional part in her young life. An interesting snippet of information was overheard only a few miles from their destination.

'I'm so glad you married Terese, Tio Manuel,' the

talkative little imp positively grinned towards her uncle from her solitary perch on the edge of the rear seat. With an arm leaning against the top of both Manuel and Terese's seat her face was only inches away from both of theirs. 'I like her much better than Emilia,' Isabella pronounced happily. 'Even Abuelita thinks Emilia *aburrida*. Abuelita will be very pleased with Terese as your *esposa*, Tio. Emilia will be—disappointed, perhaps,' she concluded sedately.

'I make my own decisions, *pequeña*,' Manuel replied tolerantly. 'You must remember not to speak in a mixture of Spanish and English,' he chastised, and directed a somewhat stern glance via the rear-vision mirror.

'*Si*, Tio Manuel,' Isabella agreed in a subdued voice, and turned to Terese. 'I am sorry, Terese.'

She spared the child a sympathetic glance. 'There's no need to apologise,' she smiled. 'I'm not quite so ignorant of the Spanish language as your uncle would have you believe. Am I right in believing that you said your grandmother thinks Emilia is a little wearisome, and that that good lady will be more pleased with me as Tio Manuel's wife—*si*?'

'*Si*, Terese,' Isabella concurred with the beginnings of a smile. 'Do you really understand Spanish?'

'Only a few words,' Terese chuckled in reply. 'There was a Spanish boy at the hospital with compound fractures of both legs. He wanted to learn as much English as he could so that when he returned to school he could better understand his lessons.'

'Were you in hospital too?' Isabella questioned with large round eyes.

'I am—was——' Terese hurriedly corrected herself. 'I was a nurse at the Royal Children's Hospital.'

44

Heavens, was it only three days since she'd left that establishment?

The little girl moved on her seat excitedly. 'Did you wear a uniform and give those horrid injections?'

Terese laughed lightheartedly. 'Those horrid injections, as you call them, are very necessary sometimes, poppet.'

'Perhaps I shall be a nurse too, when I grow up,' Isabella pondered thoughtfully, and enquired of her uncle, 'What do you think, Tio Manuel?'

'I think you will have changed your mind at least a dozen times by then, *chica*,' he smiled gently as he drew the car to a halt in the parking area. 'We have arrived. Come, the nursery slopes and a further lesson, *pequeña*.'

Isabella scrambled quickly out to stand beside Terese. 'After the lesson and we have eaten, may we build a snowman, Tio?'

Manuel chuckled and his face creased attractively as he viewed his niece across the sleek bonnet of the car. 'I begin to think the building of a snowman holds more of an attraction for you than the skiing lesson—which is why we have come here today, *no*?'

'*Si*, but the last time we came you said we could, and we couldn't afterwards because Emilia had a headache, and——'

'I remember, *chica*,' he sympathised in a voice that was more deeply accented than usual. 'After lunch we will the three of us build a snowman that is as big as we can make it. But first the lesson, hmmn?'

So, Terese reflected musingly, Emilia's presence had not been an unqualified success. It appeared from what little she had been able to glean from Isabella's happy chattering that Emilia had been brought to Manuel's attention as suitable wife-material by his mother, *and* fairly recently. What puzzled her was that Manuel had in spite of his decision to marry and produce a family dismissed such a suitable prospective bride.

Up the side of the mountain they went, and when Isabella was deposited safely on the nursery slopes Manuel took over the role of instructor. Terese had thought to stand on the sideline giving Isabella encouragement, but much to her dismay she found Manuel intended she also should take part in the lesson. Oh, darn her honesty— she should never have admitted ignorance!

It was somewhat galling to catch the amused gleam in her husband's eye as she slipped ignominiously down on to her rear for the umpteenth time and slid to a halt at his feet. She would have bruises upon existing bruises at this rate, and be as stiff as could be tomorrow. She smiled sweetly, however, as he helped her to her feet yet again, but the look in her eye promised retaliation in the near future. The building of a snowman and snowball-time was getting sweeter with every passing minute!

Their breath appeared as light misty puffs on the chill air, and everywhere Terese looked she could see snow speckled with bright splashes of colour—the green of the trees, the red gold black and orange of fashionable ski-wear. It was an intoxicating sight.

Isabella's excited cries of triumph were well deserved when she slid down the slope for the first time without landing in a flurried heap. Again and again she practised, and her delight at being able to please her uncle brought a strange tightening to Terese's throat. How could such a man command the love and adoration of this engagingly perceptive child?

The ski-lodge was well filled with a mixture of tourists

and skiers, all of whom seemed to welcome the warmth and the appetizing food available. As they sipped hot coffee after an excellent meal, Terese thought rather hollowly that to any onlookers the three of them must present a happy family unit. Manuel was at his most charming and cast her a seemingly fond glance from time to time, and if she could have met him in different circumstances she might have found him likeable. Dear God, what was she thinking! This guise of affability barely went skin-deep—assumed for the benefit of his niece. To think otherwise was utterly incomprehensible.

His hand clasped her elbow lightly as they threaded their way towards the foyer, and once outside Isabella tugged Manuel's hand as she laughingly led him with as much speed as she could muster away from the lodge. Manuel began to chuckle with every evidence of good humour and took Terese's hand, which try as she might she could not pull free, and he didn't loosen his hold until Isabella had chosen the site on which to build their snowman.

Terese had to agree that Don Nieve was indeed a first-class effort. Adorned with her scarf, Isabella's mittens bunched strategically to resemble buttons on an imaginary coat and Manuel's scarf wound round its head, not forgetting eyes nose and mouth made up from pieces of chocolate Manuel produced, it seemed almost a shame to knock it down. But knock it down they did with well-aimed snowballs, and when it was no more than a shapeless mound of snow they directed snowballs at each other.

Isabella derived great pleasure from this exercise and dissolved into giggles each time a snowball crumbled against her. Terese scored revenge on Manuel with a few well-aimed balls of snow, and there followed a steady pelting which permitted little chance of evening up the score until Manuel declared a truce and led them back to the ski-lodge for hot drinks before beginning the drive home.

Terese contented herself to be an interested listener for most of the homeward journey, lapsing into contemplative silence as she thought of Steve and worried how he was managing on his own. She would telephone before dinner and tell him she would be there tomorrow, unescorted by Santanas in the Daimler if she could manage it. But first she had to get through this evening, and she entertained no doubts in that direction. Her husband for some unknown reason of his own—and certainly it couldn't have been anything remotely resembling consideration—had permitted her to sleep through the previous night undisturbed. Tonight there would be little hope of escaping his passionate lovemaking, and the mere thought of sharing such intimacy sent an involuntary shiver through her body.

'You are cold?'

The sound of Manuel's voice caught her unawares and the startled look she cast in his direction was unwittingly revealing.

'Sometimes it does not pay,' he drawled sardonically, 'to give some matters much thought, *querida*.'

Terese drew a deep breath and forced a slight smile to her lips. 'Is mind-reading listed among your innumerable talents, Manuel Delgado?'

'Shame on you, Terese Delgado,' he countered lightly, and the dark gleam he directed across the brief space between them left Terese in no doubt as to his deliberate attempt to ruffle her composure.

'I have done nothing for which I should feel shame,

48

mi esposo,' she replied with intended emphasis, and for Isabella's benefit she laughed softly and wrinkled her nose at him.

'Your accent is charming,' Manuel allowed wryly.

'Why, thank you,' she returned whimsically.

Terese helped Isabella pack the leather holdall with the few possessions she needed to take back to boarding-school, brightly expressing her admiration of the smart uniform the little girl had donned after their early evening meal. The thought of having to face Manuel across the dinner table each evening and enduring his wry cynicism was more than daunting, and the prospect of the week ahead loomed long and interminable.

Somehow Terese had imagined the school would be a considerable distance away, but it seemed that in no time at all they were turning in between high stone pillars and slowing to a halt on the crest of a wide curving driveway. Inside the main hall Isabella was entrusted into the care of Sister Mary Imelda, who at Isabella's request gave permission for the child to take Terese, and Señor Delgado if he wished, on a brief tour of inspection. Terese envied Isabella her philosophical acceptance when it came time for them to go, and the quick hug she gave the child was genuinely warm and affectionate.

She offered not a word by way of conversation during the short drive back, and divested of her coat inside the house she preceded Manuel into the *sala,* accepting the glass of sherry he handed her. She chose a deep-cushioned armchair and sank into it, watching cautiously as he took a similar chair opposite.

'There is nothing you wish to know?' Manuel queried,

49

and his eyes narrowed slightly at her defensive attitude.

'Not really,' she replied, 'except what time breakfast is in the morning?'

'Sofia serves mine at seven, although there is no need for you to rise so early.'

She shot him a cross look. 'I don't intend spending most of the morning in bed. Seven o'clock will suit me fine.'

'As you wish,' he inclined his head mockingly, then withdrew a slim case from the inside breast pocket of his jacket and extracted a cheroot. 'Isabella mentioned her grandmother on at least two occasions today.' He paused as he held the flame close to his lips, then exhaled with satisfaction. 'Madre spends much of her time travelling—she likes to keep in close contact with her kin, most of whom are well scattered throughout the globe. At the time of both Vicente and Esteban's death she was in Melbourne assuring herself that Isabella was content in my care.'

Terese felt a sudden shaft of pain as he mentioned the reason for her being here, a form of human revenge, and her eyes sparked alive and expressively eloquent.

'There was a dual purpose in the visit,' Manuel continued significantly, and his dark eyes raked her features. 'She has considered it more than time I took a wife, and Emilia Gomez is the fifth or sixth young woman to accompany Madre on one of her many excursions. At the moment they are in Brisbane enjoying the warmer climate, and I expect them here within the next two or three weeks.'

'Your mother will hardly be appreciative of the fact that you've married without her approval—especially me,' she observed somewhat dryly. This proposed visit would indeed place the cat among the pigeons!

Manuel's eyebrows rose a fraction. 'Why you—*especially*?'

'I would have thought that was obvious!'

'The only thing that is obvious would be your stupidity in blatantly declaring to my mother your connection with Steve Montgomerie.'

Terese immediately felt her anger rise. 'You expect me to deny it?'

'I don't imagine you will be called upon to admit or deny anything,' he answered brusquely. 'You are my wife, and my mother will welcome you as such. Undoubtedly she will admire your feminine wiles in succeeding where others have failed,' he concluded wryly.

She watched the slight smile tug the corners of his mouth and felt far from amused. 'Emilia Gomez will credit me with using every devious method there is, and as she probably fancied herself in the role, I'm not exactly going to be her favourite person!'

Manuel shrugged his shoulders and his expression became faintly bored. 'My dear Terese, you are the very antithesis of Emilia Gomez. I shouldn't imagine her hostility, if any, will bother you.'

She held his gaze and refrained from speaking, although her silence was as eloquent as any words could have been.

'I am my own man, *mi esposa*,' he commented albeit cynically, 'and answerable to no one. Only a fool would suppose otherwise.'

'That is what you will remain,' Terese declared quietly, 'and in the end it will be you who is the fool.'

He studied her with deliberate ease for what seemed an age, and when he spoke his voice was dangerously soft. 'You seem impervious to the limitations of my temper.'

'We hate each other,' Terese said sombrely. 'It can never be otherwise.'

'I would far rather have you hate me honestly, Terese,' he said wryly. 'Emilia, like countless others before her, would have married me for my wealth and social prestige.'

Suddenly she felt weary, emotionally at odds with herself and the complex cynical man seated a few feet away. With concentrated effort she sipped the wine in her glass and then stood to her feet. 'I must telephone Steve.'

'You can use the extension in my study. There is paperwork which requires my attention for perhaps an hour or more,' he intimated smoothly.

Terese followed him silently and stood as she dialled Steve's number, aware that Manuel had seated himself behind the large desk and was unashamedly listening to her conversation. As she replaced the receiver she shot him a baleful glance which had no effect whatever, for he continued to regard her steadily.

'Your loyalty is admirable.'

'Steve more than deserves it. I consider having to suffer your impossible tyranny for a few weeks a small price to pay to ensure his peace of mind.'

A strange silence followed her words—a silence that seemed to fill the room until Terese felt almost afraid to move.

'What makes you think I will let you go?'

His voice was too quiet—like the calm before the storm, she thought a trifle hysterically.

'You must know that I am bound to you only until Steve dies—after that nothing will keep me here,' she declared with a flash of spirit that quickly fled at the glimpse of terrible anger in his ebony-dark eyes.

'Have you not considered by that time there is a possibility you will be *encinta*—with child? What then?' he pursued relentlessly.

She fixed her eyes on the onyx paperweight on top of his desk and refused to lift her gaze.

'What then, Terese? An abortion?' His voice was silk-smooth and dangerous. 'Or did you intend to have the child and hope to keep me in ignorance of its existence?'

She looked at him then and felt a clutch of fear knot her stomach at the icy anger evident in every line of his features. 'I hadn't given it much thought.' Heavens, was that her voice? It sounded strange, almost as if it belonged to someone else. She felt as if she were floating, a disembodied spectator. Perhaps if she closed her eyes and opened them again all this would turn out to be a horrid dream.

'You are taking precautions to safeguard against such a pregnancy?'

Terese shook her head and was unable to tear her eyes away from his. 'No,' she whispered shakily. Her concern was solely for Steve, and she had blindly disregarded her own welfare. What little she knew of Manuel Delgado should have warned her that he would not allow her to escape easily—'what I have, I hold,' he had said. The idea of staying within his hold for a lifetime was something she had never envisaged, and she almost wept at her own stupidity.

'I have your word that you will not do so?'

Terese blinked back the tears that threatened to well behind her eyelids and held his gaze with difficulty. 'I don't believe you have the right to demand that.' She turned unsteadily and almost ran from the room in her haste to put as much distance as possible between them.

In the entrance lobby she hesitated fractionally—the thought of viewing television or going upstairs to bed was equally abhorrent. The need to get out of the house was paramount, and without thinking of the cold or inclement weather she slipped out the front door.

The air was heavy and oppressive as if a storm was about to unleash its fury, and a distant roll of thunder merely heightened its imminence. Terese shivered and stood hesitantly before stepping cautiously out on to the driveway.

It seemed she hadn't taken more than a dozen steps when there was a low canine growl that brought her to a quivering standstill. One didn't argue with that sort of growl—its menacing pitch was sufficient warning not to take another step. A flashlight blinded her and she uttered a startled cry as the animal brushed against her.

There followed a sharp command and the flashlight lowered to reveal Santanas reflected in its light.

'Señora!' Santanas' shock at seeing her alone in the grounds was obvious, and his explanation concerning his nightly inspection with Baltasar prior to locking up was both voluble and apologetic. Whereupon Baltasar was properly introduced, and Terese viewed him with considerable respect while her hand was licked and a wet nose nudged at her arm.

'You may now pat him if you wish. He will never question your presence again,' Santanas explained quietly, and Terese put a tentative hand out towards the animal's head. A soft whimper of sound greeted this gesture and she watched Baltasar inch forward until his head brushed her hand, and he continued to sit there while she fondled his fur. Dogs of any kind she had had little to do with, and a full-grown Alsatian guard-dog took some getting used to—especially when she had believed herself about to be attacked only minutes before.

'I will escort you back to the house. The Señor will undoubtedly insist upon a glass of *coñac*—a good remedy for shock and the cold,' Santanas evinced with concern.

Terese started visibly. 'No, there is no need to disturb the Señor, Santanas. He is working in the study, and I have come to no harm.' The last thing she wanted was a further confrontation with her forceful husband.

It was obvious Santanas thought otherwise, and even her assurance that she would go straight upstairs and run a hot steaming bath did little to dissuade him from informing Manuel.

Terese didn't wait for the outcome, and was unaware of the puzzled frown that was directed after her as she fled hurriedly to her room. Several minutes later she began to relax as the bath filled and there was no sign of Manuel. If he had intended storming into the room to bring all kinds of Spanish ire upon her head he would surely have done so by now. With more speed than care she flung off her clothes and slipped into the steamy scented water, remembering at the last moment to push her hair hastily beneath the bath-cap to prevent it from becoming damp.

After a luxurious soak she emerged pink and deliciously warm. With a towel wrapped sarong-wise about her slim form she stepped into the bedroom and came to an abrupt halt.

'You don't appear to be suffering too drastically from your encounter with Baltasar.' Manuel raked her features with a thoroughness that brought heightened colour flooding to her cheeks.

'Santanas told you,' she stated with remarkable calm.

'Of course. Did you imagine that he would not?'

She shrugged negligently, reluctant to take the steps that would bring her close to where he was sitting on the edge of the bed. 'I don't need that,' she cast an idle hand towards the glass of *coñac* he held in his hand.

'Perhaps not all,' he agreed, standing to his feet. 'But you will drink some of it nonetheless.'

Feeling far from calm, she accepted the glass from his outstretched hand and obediently took a few sips.

'Why did you venture outside without so much as a coat to protect you from the cold?'

'I needed some fresh air,' Terese essayed obliquely, fixing her eyes on the third button of his dark blue shirt. Gone was the jacket, and he had removed his tie and unbuttoned the two top buttons of the expensive silk shirt. Dark curling hairs were visible, and she couldn't tear her eyes away. The brandy must be going straight to her head! With a mental shake she dragged her eyes back to the glass in her hand and took a too generous sip of the fiery liquid. Tears sprang to her eyes as she coughed and regained her breath, and by then the glass had been taken and Manuel had drained the contents. A terrible apathy assailed her limbs as his hands curved round her bare shoulders.

'What are you going to do?' she asked shakily, and ran the tip of her tongue nervously along her lower lip.

'Make love to you.' There was a quirk of amusement in his voice. 'What did you imagine I had in mind?'

Terese held his gaze for a few seconds, then her eyes slid away.

'Poor *niña*,' Manuel murmured wryly as he bent his head down to hers.

She quickly turned her face away and his lips brushed

her cheek, then she winced as a hand tangled in her hair and a swift downward tug brought her head up so that she had little choice but to look at him.

'You don't hesitate to take what you want,' she said bitterly.

'Indecision is not one of my traits, *querida*. The man who patiently waits outside his own bedroom door is no man at all. You would ensure that I waited, would you not?'

'You'd wait for ever!'

'For ever is a long time,' Manuel said dryly.

'I'll never be yours willingly, Manuel Delgado—you must know that.'

'No?' he drawled sardonically.

She felt the warmth of his breath against her forehead and tightly pressed her lips together as his mouth sought hers. The cry that began deep in her throat never escaped her lips as the bruising intensity of his mouth parted hers and punished until she gasped for breath.

'You cannot continually fight against me. This mobile mouth,' he traced it with an idle finger and Terese tried not to shiver beneath his touch, 'denotes a passionate nature. Even now your heart beats more quickly.'

'If it does, it's fear—not passion,' she declared heatedly, hating the blush that swiftly coloured her cheeks as he loosened the towel and caressed the soft fullness of her breasts. Her eyes flashed angrily. 'I'm forced to endure your lovemaking, but don't expect me to enjoy it!'

'Oh, but I intend that you shall,' he smiled gently, and there was a dangerous sensuality in his voice, a sense of purpose that was disquieting.

Terese forced a grimace of distaste and shrugged lightly. 'Your conceit is staggering!'

Manuel chuckled softly as his eyes roamed from the top of her head to the tips of her toes. 'Come now, surely you can do better than that? How about "assured, overbearingly bossy, impossibly arrogant—brutally cruel"?'

'All of those, and more.'

'But never kind, is that it?'

Honesty compelled her to answer truthfully. 'You're kind with Isabella.' And patient and compassionate, she added silently.

His mouth descended on hers, the kiss deepening as his lips demanded a response, and her murmur of protest was ignored as he swung her down on to the bed.

CHAPTER FOUR

TERESE awoke next morning to the sound of the shower hissing softly in the bathroom. A quick glance revealed an empty pillow beside her and she turned in the carelessly-pulled bedcovers to reach for the bed-lamp switch. Ten minutes before seven, and if she was to sit down to breakfast with Manuel it was time to rise and shine. Wasting little time over her ablutions she hastily showered and dressed in dark brown slacks with matching jumper and added a fashionable light tan jerkin made of soft suede.

Manuel was already seated when she entered the dining-room, and if he was surprised she had kept her voiced intention to share his early breakfast he didn't show it.

'*Buenos dias,*' he greeted tolerantly as he poured his

coffee and put aside the newspaper.

'Good morning,' she replied politely, and gestured towards the folded morning paper. 'Please go ahead and read—I shan't mind.'

'What do you wish to eat? Sofia was not expecting you until later.'

'Just toast and coffee,' Terese assured him with a slight smile. 'I don't like to burden my stomach so early in the day.' Deftly she poured herself some coffee and took a slice of toast from the rack.

'You intend visiting your stepfather today?'

'Yes.' Her reply was coolly determined and she eyed him a trifle defiantly.

'Ready to do battle, *mi esposa?*' Manuel mocked softly. 'Did I not agree that you could go? If you will tell me what time you wish to leave, I will instruct Santanas to have the car ready.'

He looked totally invincible and every inch the successful businessman. Immaculately dressed, he favoured a cream cashmere jumper beneath his jacket which succeeded in emphasizing the powerful breadth of his shoulders, and there was nothing in his manner to give hint to the passion he had displayed last night.

'About nine—and I would prefer to catch a tram,' Terese declared purposefully.

'But you will not,' Manuel voiced brusquely, and shot her a compelling look from those dark eyes of his. 'We are to dine out this evening,' he continued. 'A business associate of mine—a fellow Spaniard. It will be a formal affair and therefore you must make use of one of my charge accounts if you possess nothing suitable to wear.'

'I'm to make an impression,' Terese deduced succinctly.

'You manage to do that very successfully without even trying,' he remarked dryly.

'I'm not sure that's meant to be a compliment,' she contemplated speculatively.

'Santanas will collect you before four o'clock— earlier, if you wish to do some shopping,' he bade firmly.

'Oh, I shall,' she assured him, warning sweetly— 'You're taking rather a risk allowing me carte blanche with your credit card. I might go berserk and buy a complete new wardrobe.'

One dark eyebrow raised itself above the faintly cynical glance he spared in her direction. 'I don't imagine it would ruin me.'

Terese felt suddenly gauche and rather childish.

With the air of a man with other things on his mind, he eased his lengthy frame from the chair and drained the last of his coffee. Coolly he strode the few feet to where she was seated and bent his head down to hers, his lips coming to rest on the warm scented skin of her neck just beneath an earlobe.

'You—you savage!' she exclaimed in outraged indignation seconds after his mouth sought a vulnerable hollow at the base of her throat.

'Ah, *querida*,' he mocked gently.

'I bruise easily.' She swung dark blazing eyes to meet his.

'Shock easily, too,' he murmured softly as he placed a fleeting kiss to her lips. '*Adios, mi esposa.*'

Terese refrained from bidding him farewell and her eyes were particularly eloquent as they followed his tall frame to the door. Vexedly she rubbed a hand back and forth over the tingling area where he had teasingly bitten. Really, he was the most impossibly arrogant, *possessive* man she had ever met!

It was barely eight o'clock and much too early to leave. The thought that she would dismiss Manuel's instruction and catch a tram flashed through her mind, but determined as she was not to be subjected to his will, she felt strangely diffident at deliberately arousing his anger. It seemed as if they had been constantly at war for most of the weekend, apart from the hours spent in Isabella's company, and each conflict had proved him to be formidably ruthless.

Sofia entered the room and wished Terese a surprised 'good morning', then began clearing the breakfast table.

Terese stood to her feet and the words left her lips scarcely before she had time to think. 'Is there something I could do to help? Santanas and I are not leaving until nine o'clock.'

Perhaps her voice or her expression appeared a little woebegone, for Sofia paused from her task of stacking dishes on to a tray and cast her a surprisingly sympathetic glance.

'Perhaps the Señora would like to explore the house? Maria would enjoy to accompany you, and you may wish to consult with me over a preference for tomorrow evening's meal?'

Terese shook her head quickly and smiled. 'Oh, no. You have been with my—husband for some time. He mentioned that you manage very satisfactorily, so I see no reason to interfere. In any case,' she paused a little awkwardly, 'I am not very conversant with his preference of food, and would much rather leave the choice to you. But if you could spare Maria for a while, I would like to look through the house more thoroughly.'

It was evident this met with Sofia's approval, for Terese sensed that the woman had been apprehensive of a new mistress and wary of any changes that might be demanded in the running of the household.

'*Si, señora.*' The words were spoken with relieved contentment and a smile warmed her features as she picked up the tray. 'I will send Maria to you.'

Terese had seen Maria only briefly early Saturday evening when they had returned from Healesville—an attractive-looking girl with neatly-groomed dark hair, lovely eyes and a neat figure, whose age was perhaps sixteen. Quietly-spoken and very respectful—too respectful, Terese thought wryly after ten minutes in her company, for Maria displayed a courtesy resembling that of a lowly maid in presence of royalty!

Together they went through the upstairs apartments —and they were apartments, it seemed to Terese, with each of the eight bedrooms having bathroom and toilet facilities en suite. There was a lounge—or perhaps it was intended as a family room, upstairs, comfortably furnished with numerous armchairs, wall-units neatly filled with books, a writing-desk, reading-lamps and expensive stereo equipment. The rooms downstairs were obviously designed for formal entertaining. The lounge was tremendous in size and at first glance looked adequate enough to accommodate forty guests with comparative ease. Furniture and fittings were superbly elegant, and the Mediterranean influence was remarkably evident throughout the entire house. The dining-room brought a vivid recollection of her first meal with Manuel —even the size of the table was daunting, for there were no fewer than eight chairs placed on either side of its length.

The only room Maria didn't enter was Manuel's study, and Terese had no particular wish to re-acquaint herself with that room! Of all the downstairs rooms, the *sala* was her favourite. It looked out over the gardens at the rear of the house and was situated to receive as much of the winter sun as possible. There were sliding glass doors leading out on to a paved patio with steps down on to the lawn where in summer white-painted wrought-iron garden furniture was placed beneath the shade of the trees, Maria told her informatively. Obviously Sofia's pride and joy, the kitchen was large and modern with every up-to-date electrical appliance available. There was a three-car garage attached to the side of the house, and behind this were the Santanas' living quarters, very cleverly designed around a central courtyard to give almost total privacy.

All told, it spelt the luxury of a wealthy man's indulgence to a style of living he could well afford.

'How long have your parents been with Señor Delgado, Maria?' Terese questioned curiously. Their tour of inspection was completed and they were standing together at the foot of the staircase.

'For many years, *señora*,' Maria answered with a smile. 'But not always here. First we were at the small stud-farm near Dandenong, then the Señor built this big house—five, perhaps six years ago.'

'Are you Australian-born? I'm sorry—I don't mean to be rude,' Terese apologised hastily.

Maria shook her head and reassured politely. 'Of course not. No,' she continued, 'my parents came to Australia already in the employ of Señor Delgado. My grandfather, my father—they have worked all their lives for the Delgado family.'

'Oh, I see,' Terese commented faintly.

'The Delgado family is a very honourable one, *señora*.'

Ah yes, Terese thought rather sceptically—honour and tradition and noble Spanish pride, with one Manuel

Sebastian Rafael Delgado at its pinnacle, no less.

'Is there anywhere else the Señora wishes to go? The gardens, perhaps?' Maria questioned quietly. 'It is wet underfoot from the rain overnight, but we could keep to the path.'

Terese shook her head and declined. 'Not this morning, Maria. It's almost time for me to leave with your father. Thank you for conducting me through the house,' she concluded with a friendly smile.

'It was a pleasure, *señora*,' Maria acknowledged, then turned and disappeared towards the kitchen.

Terese ran lightly upstairs and collected a coat and shoulder-bag from her dressing-room, brushed a comb hurriedly through her hair and added a touch of lipstick to her lips before moving quickly down to where Santanas was patiently waiting in the entrance lobby.

'Good morning, *señora*,' he greeted her formally.

Oh, heavens, if only she could say, 'Please don't call me that—Terese, or simply Mrs Delgado if you must!' But 'Good morning, Santanas,' she demurely replied.

Together they walked down the steps to the maroon-coloured Daimler, and as Santanas held open the rear door Terese suppressed an expressive sigh and slipped into the back seat. All this formality and protocol was beginning to prove irksome!

'Does the Señora wish to drive directly to Heidelberg?' Santanas asked as he negotiated the driveway and moved into a steady stream of traffic.

If you only knew what the Señora wished, Terese thought, your respectful eyes would pop right out of your respectful head! 'I have some shopping to do,' she voiced aloud. 'Perhaps it might be as well to get it over and done with now. If you could drop me off outside Myer's, and allow me half an hour or so?'

'Si, señora. After thirty minutes I will drive around the block until you appear outside the main entrance.'

Terese almost choked. 'Thank you, Santanas.' Gone were the days when she had to worry over finding parking space and change for the meter, obviously!

Ten minutes later she slipped inside the front entrance of Myer's emporium, one of the largest department stores in the city, and made her way to the correct floor. Manuel had stressed formal attire, but how formal? Something more elegant than a hostess skirt and top, of that she was sure. She shied away from anything too bright, choosing after much searching a long gown of floral-patterned chiffon over cream silk. It had a demure neckline and long sleeves gathered into a wide buttoned cuff at the wrists, and the autumn tonings complemented her dark auburn hair and creamy skin. She already possessed a gold oroton evening bag and evening sandals, but some new perfume was a whim she indulged herself.

It was close on an hour later when she emerged from the main entrance on the ground floor, and right on cue the Daimler with Santanas at the wheel pulled into the kerb.

'I'm afraid I was longer than I expected,' Terese apologised as Santanas relieved her of the packages and placed them in the car.

'The Señora was remarkably quick,' Santanas offered with a slight smile as he swung the large car away from the kerb.

Terese shot him a dubious glance, not quite sure whether he was attempting a touch of humour. Perhaps he was, for there was a twinkle in his dark eyes that she could see reflected by the rear-vision mirror.

They reached Heidelberg and turned down the street

leading to Steve's house. Terese could almost see the slight twitch of several curtains as the opulent car slowed to a halt and imagined the interest it would cause as Santanas quickly moved round to open the door for her. The tongues would wag in tireless speculation over both morning and afternoon cups of tea for days to come!

'I'll return at three-thirty, *señora*,' Santanas offered politely. 'The shopping I will have Maria unpack on my return home.'

'Thank you, Santanas,' Terese murmured gratefully. 'You have made things much easier for me than had I come by tram.'

'The Señor would never permit——'

'I know,' she interrupted his faintly scandalised diatribe. '*Adios*,' she said placatingly as she turned towards the gate.

The pathway to the front door was short, and by the time she reached the porch Steve was standing in the open doorway waiting to greet her.

'Terese!' He hugged her to him with enthusiastic affection. 'You're okay, honey?' Anxious hazel eyes searched hers.

'Of course,' she laughed up at him and put on her cheerful face—the one she could summon at will for her young hospital patients. 'Why shouldn't I be?'

'Your husband didn't object to you coming here?' Steve queried intently.

'Hey,' she wrinkled her nose at him and forced a light sparkle into her voice, 'what is this? Aren't you going to ask me in?'

Steve flung an arm about her shoulders and dropped a kiss on top of her burnished hair. 'This is as much your home as it is mine—you know that.' He chuckled in good humour. 'Ask you in, indeed!'

'Have you had breakfast?'

'Yes, but we'll have coffee, shall we? You can tell me how you enjoy living in that huge mansion with your noble Spaniard.'

Terese detected the bitterness in his voice with a sinking heart. 'Didn't you glimpse the opulent Daimler saloon which transported me here this morning?' She placed one of her arms about his waist and hugged him gently. 'I arrived in style—with a chauffeur behind the wheel, no less! Manuel has handed me credit cards for two of the largest department stores in town, and I'm to have a monthly allowance as well.'

'Possessions, gifts,' Steve dismissed. 'What about the man himself?' he queried piercingly, not entirely convinced.

Dear heaven, he looked weary! Terese disengaged her arm as he sank down into a chair and tried not to let her anxiety show. 'Any man who is as successful as Manuel must possess a certain ruthlessness,' she offered quietly. 'I've found he can be kind, and compassionate.' But not with me, she added silently.

Steve held her gaze unwaveringly. 'Are you happy?'

'As happy as I can expect to be,' she answered evenly, adding—'Manuel is indisputably Spanish in his outlook despite having lived in Australia for several years, and he becomes displeased whenever I display any of the total independence I have accepted as my right for some time now. Aren't you more contented knowing I shan't be alone?'

Steve caught the slight anguish in her voice and reached out to clasp her hand reassuringly. 'Yes,' he said simply, then smiled. 'I've a yen to see the ocean today. Your Mini is still here—have we time?'

Terese hurriedly bent and dropped a kiss at the edge of his mouth as her eyes filled with tears. 'Your wish is my command,' she smiled gently as she moved away to pour coffee from the percolator into cups.

'Mrs Scott seems to be revelling in her role as house-keeper-cum-watchdog. Very unobtrusive,' Steve commented as Terese sat down opposite him at the kitchen table. 'Doesn't chit-chat, and best of all, doesn't look at me with a mixture of sympathy and pity in her eyes. Now, don't argue,' he remonstrated gently. 'I know you intend coming every day, but I want to spend that time *with* you—not following you about the house as you clean and tidy up.'

'The men in my life seem determined to make me a lady of leisure,' Terese stated quizzically as she sipped the delicious brew. 'My husband employs Santanas as manservant and chauffeur, whose wife Sofia does all the cooking, and their daughter Maria attends to the housework.' She wrinkled her nose expressively. 'All I'm expected to do is play the part of a socialite.'

'I'm pleased you appear to be so well taken care of, my dear. Your husband obviously commands a well-run household—for which you should be duly grateful. In any case, there'll be the patter of tiny feet to occupy your time before long. I would enjoy your leisure while you can!' His hazel eyes twinkled unrepentantly. 'Spaniards are reputedly proud family men—I predict within six years you'll be a doting mama to at least three little Delgados.'

'I refuse to contemplate the patter of tiny feet—to-day,' she laughed, and attempted to keep her voice light. If he should guess, she despaired inwardly. 'While you finish your coffee I'll get the car from the garage and check the fuel gauge. Any ideas from which point you wish to view the ocean?'

'The Mornington Peninsula,' Steve stated at once, and Terese knew exactly where he meant. In summers gone by they had shared many a picnic along the shores from Frankston down as far as Sorrento near the southern tip.

'I almost forgot to mention it,' Steve revealed suddenly. 'Meg rang this morning and asked if you could contact her at home before lunch—she's on duty this afternoon. Something about tickets she'd bought a few weeks ago for some show.'

Terese cast him a startled glance as she moved towards the telephone. 'Oh dear, I'd forgotten all about that in the excitement of being rushed off my feet into matrimony.' Hastily she dialled Meg's number and tried to remember for which night the tickets had been purchased. Unless she was mistaken, it was Tuesday—tomorrow evening.

'Terese? You'd forgotten, hadn't you?'

'Sorry, Meg,' she sounded contrite. 'Yes, I had. Can you find someone else to use my ticket?'

'Well, that's the problem,' Meg twinkled humorously. 'Suffice to say that I've tried. Do you think that utterly gorgeous Spaniard of yours might spare you for all of five hours?'

Terese deliberated with slight trepidation, knowing Manuel would adamantly refuse if she asked, and the thought of leaving a message with Sofia explaining her absence would have formidable consequences on her return.

'Surely he would understand?' Meg continued plausibly. 'The tickets were expensive, and besides, you were very keen to go. Can you check with him and ring me back?'

'Yes, I'll ring you early tomorrow morning. I don't like to contact him at work,' Terese explained hesitantly.

Meg chuckled lightly. 'Very wise, my dear. Wait until this evening when he's been wined and dined, then use the subtle art of feminine persuasion.'

'Is that what it's called?' Terese couldn't resist an attempt at humour despite the curling sensation that began deep inside her stomach at the very thought of her husband's sensual expertise.

'Half your luck, Terese,' Meg responded enviously.

If you only knew, Terese thought silently. With the semblance of gaiety she bade Meg goodbye and replaced the receiver.

It was cold but fine as they drove southwards along the Nepean highway. The coastline revealed a grey swelling sea with angry white crests, and as they approached Dromana it began to rain. The decision to stop for lunch was mutual, and they chose a café which served freshly-made pancakes and scones. Topped with jam and fresh-whipped cream, accompanied with steaming coffee, it was a veritable feast. Afterwards they wandered arm-in-arm past the shop windows, and there was a sadness in that each knew they would never stroll along this particular street together again. Terese endeavoured to be bright and cheerful, but deep inside her heart felt as if it were breaking into tiny pieces.

The heavy rain began as they left Portsea en route back to the city well past three o'clock in the afternoon, and there was no possible hope that she could be in suburban Heidelberg at the time she had arranged with Santanas. He was in for a long wait, she perceived wryly. On the outskirts of Frankston the aged Mini reluctantly gave up the struggle to keep the water out of its distributor and the engine simply cut out, forcing Terese to bring the car to a halt at the side of the road.

By four-thirty she had achieved very little other than to have the car towed to a nearby garage, where a slow-moving, unobliging mechanic declined to provide any help other than to shake his head and mutter unintelligibly beneath his breath. It appeared there was some mechanical malfunction that was impossible to correct without a spare part which wasn't available and couldn't be obtained until the following day. Terese gnashed her teeth and tried to contain her temper with concentrated effort.

A telephone call and an explanation to Sofia brought further worries of a different kind, for Manuel had despatched a message via his secretary that he would be arriving home an hour earlier than usual, and Santanas had been telephoning at half-hourly intervals from Heidelberg and was most concerned.

To top it all off—as if anything else were needed, she reflected crossly—they arrived at the station in time to see a city-bound train leave the platform. It just wasn't turning out to be her day at all!

It was exactly seven o'clock when she stepped inside the Daimler after seeing Steve comfortably settled, and twenty minutes later she positively leapt from the car before Santanas had the opportunity to alight and open the door. A worried Sofia greeted her, but Terese didn't pause for more than a second as she ran across the marble-tiled floor and ascended the stairs with as much speed as she could manage.

By the time she reached the bedroom she had unbuttoned her coat and was beginning to tug at the knot of hair on top of her head. Such was her hurry she didn't see Manuel standing inside the room until she almost collided with his solid frame.

'Oh!' Her fright was all too real as she shot him a startled look and her heart sank as she glimpsed the cold anger emanating from his tautly-chiselled features. 'I'm sorry—I can be ready in twenty minutes,' she began hurriedly, and her eyes darted to the bed where Maria had laid out her new dress.

'You have fifteen,' Manuel clipped brusquely. 'None of which I would advise you to waste. Sofia has relayed details of your misadventure—*your* explanation I will hear later.'

So—she was to have a brief respite from his anger! Terese breathed a small sigh of relief as she ran to her dressing-room and began to discard clothes with hurried abandon. The shower came close to being her quickest yet, and she blessed fate for her slight figure which required only a minimum of undergarments beneath her clothes. Make-up of necessity was minimal, and several hard strokes of the brush brought reasonable order to her hair. Where? Where was her evening bag? Frantically she searched and finally found it tucked away in a lower drawer inside the clothes-closet. Quickly she pushed inside a few necessities—there, now only shoes and—oh heavens, panty-hose! With two minutes to spare she emerged into the bedroom and quickly stepped into her dress, pulling it into place and fastening the zip-fastener with easy fluidity. A quick smoothing gesture over her hair and she was ready.

Manuel's analytical appraisal was disturbing, to say the least, and Terese knew her cheeks were flushed and her eyes over-bright as they descended the stairs and moved towards the entrance lobby where Santanas stood waiting to assist them with their coats.

Terese sat in strained silence as Manuel swung the car out from the driveway and headed along St George's Road. She had no idea where they were going, or who their hosts were to be—whether it was a large gathering or simply a few selected guests. In his present mood she felt disinclined to ask. Somehow she had expected him to demand a detailed explanation almost as soon as the Mercedes-Benz left the wide sweep of the driveway, but he appeared aloof and unapproachable as he negotiated the traffic.

After her second glass of wine—one of the finest sherries imported from the Spanish province of Jerez, their host Guillermo Cortez explained as he cajoled her to accept yet another glass before dinner—Terese began to relax slightly and took time to view circumspectly the assortment of mingling guests standing in groups about the large beautifully furnished lounge.

'Manuel—darling!'

Terese slowly turned her head to see a stunning blonde glide towards them. Rather uncharitably Terese thought her too perfectly groomed—several hours, if not the entire day must have been devoted to her appearance to have achieved such perfection.

'*Buenas tardes*, Nadine,' Manuel greeted smoothly, and Terese waited expectantly for him to perform an introduction, but when none was forthcoming she glanced curiously from Nadine to Manuel.

'I just adore it when you speak Spanish, darling,' Nadine's eyes glittered at the obvious slight, although to give the woman credit her outward composure remained unruffled. 'I am Nadine Norcroft, my dear,' she announced with false gaiety to Terese. 'It appears we must introduce ourselves.'

'So it seems,' Terese smiled slightly. 'Terese——'

'Delgado,' Manuel interjected calmly, and taking Terese's left hand he raised it and placed the gold of her wedding ring to his lips. 'My wife,' he said softly, and his eyes gleamed darkly warm and eloquent as he gazed down at her.

Terese felt the swift flood of colour that rose to her cheeks and momentarily closed her eyes in an attempt to mask the utter embarrassment she knew to be evident in their depths. How she hated him for deliberately presenting the image of an adoring husband!

'You blush easily,' Nadine remarked unkindly. 'But then Manuel's virility can be overwhelming.'

'Totally devastating,' Terese agreed obliquely. There, let Nadine make of that what she pleased!

'There have been many women in Manuel's past, my dear,' Nadine essayed sardonically. 'I hope you're not the jealous type?'

Terese lifted her gaze to meet the barely masked bitterness in the other woman's pale blue eyes. 'Not at all,' she answered honestly, and turned to Manuel with a brilliant smile. 'I have no reason to be, have I, *darling*?'

'None whatsoever, *amada*,' he granted urbanely, and Terese caught the momentary flare of mockery in the depths of his eyes. He appeared not at all disturbed and if anything he seemed to be enjoying the exchange.

Nadine let a trill of laughter escape her lips just as Guillermo Cortez announced that dinner was about to be served in the dining-room.

'Do you have to emphasize your apparent devotion so blatantly?' Terese questioned in a furious undertone as they moved leisurely after the other guests.

'Female predators of Nadine's calibre eat as hors

74

d'oeuvres little girls such as you,' Manuel drawled cynically.

'Thank you,' she acknowledged witheringly.

'So you should,' he allowed with a soft chuckle.

'I think you're perfectly despicable,' Terese tempered
the words with a sweet smile and took her place at the
table.

The meal comprised several courses during which the
conversation flowed as freely as the wine, and afterwards
when coffee was served in the lounge Terese sought a
solitary armchair in an attempt to escape Manuel's disturbing presence. The effort of presenting a compatible
front was becoming decidedly nerve-racking!

'You are finding the strain a little difficult, are you
not?'

Terese looked up and met Manuel's sardonic gaze as
he perched himself with ease on the arm of her chair.
'You're so right,' she answered solemnly, and tried not
to snatch her hand away as he leaned forward and
loosely threaded his fingers through hers.

'Poor niña,' he murmured quizzically, and touched
his lips to her temple in a gesture that brought forth all
her animosity against him.

'Words cannot describe how much I hate you!'

'Be careful, my little cat, that I do not take it upon
myself to really make you hate me.'

Terese shrugged and bit her lip as she looked down at
the broad hand that held captive her own. Its strength
was a vivid reminder of his physical superiority, and she
already had a number of bruises without adding to them.
In a low voice she asked shakily, 'What more can you
possibly do?'

His eyes narrowed and his fingers tightened painfully.

It was a great relief that at that precise moment Guillermo and Eva Cortez moved across the room to join them.

In the car at last, Terese leant her elbow against the door and tilted her head to rest against her hand. Manuel drove with swift competence through the wet dark streets, his profile stern in the reflected light. Oh, dear God, she felt tired! Tired and as jumpy as a cat on hot bricks. Steve had looked so jaundiced today that she feared the doctor's 'several weeks' were rapidly dwindling down to few more than two or three. And afterwards—how could she go on living a mockery with the man who was her husband? And children—what if there were children? Then she would be irretrievably bound to him. Their marriage vows—hers, to love honour and obey. His—to love honour and cherish. Cherish? The idea was ludicrous! Manuel Delgado would cherish no woman, and never her. Love couldn't be confused with passion—she'd already experienced the proof of that! He took what he wanted, when he wanted, with an expertise she was beginning to find difficult to resist.

The driveway was lit, and twin lamps burned brightly in welcome at either side of the massive front door. In total silence Manuel garaged the car, closed the gates and released Baltasar to roam the grounds, then together they entered the house.

As they ascended the stairs Terese waited for him to say something, at any moment expecting him to demand a full explanation of why she had not returned at the specified time that afternoon. No doubt he would make sarcastic comment with reference to the Mini breaking down—it simply added fuel to the proverbial fire that a second car associated with her family should reveal mechanical problems.

'You have the name and address of the garage where you left your car?'

Terese turned and cast him a speculative glance. In the subdued glow of the wall-light at the top of the stairs it was difficult to read much from his expression. 'Yes, I have their card in my bag,' she answered quietly.

'Very well, I shall see that arrangements are made to have it collected.'

Terese followed him into the bedroom and eyed him warily. 'What do you mean?' she queried defensively.

Manuel unfastened his jacket and hooked a thumb under the belt at his waist as he stood regarding her with vexation. 'Why question my motives?'

'Because I wouldn't put it past you to sell the Mini behind my back!'

'That would prove difficult, don't you think?' he drawled slowly, and his eyes became dark with anger. 'The papers of ownership are presumably in your name, therefore it would be your signature that is required on the appropriate form,' he concluded bluntly.

'I'm sorry,' she offered after a long silence.

'No, you're not,' Manuel observed dryly, but there was a glimmer of amusement in his voice. 'I begin to believe you enjoy our verbal recriminations. You fight me at every opportunity.'

Terese flashed him a look of dislike. 'I always will— fight you, I mean,' she amended quickly. 'In every way I can.'

'Your claws are showing, *niña*. Be careful that in trying to scratch me it is not yourself who is harmed.'

'I wish I were a man,' she brooded ruminatively as she stepped out of her shoes.

'So that you might physically assault me, is that it?' He began to chuckle and his eyes gleamed wickedly.

'What makes you think you would succeed, *querida*?'

Without pausing to think she aimed one of her shoes at him, watching in horrified fascination as he deftly caught and altered it in his grip and advanced towards her.

Terese felt like running, but there was nowhere to run to escape him, and whatever she did could only make things worse. His intention was formidably clear and he looked angry enough to carry out a thorough spanking. She wanted to cry out that she was sorry for the childishly foolish action, but no words passed her lips. Mesmerised, she couldn't tear her eyes away from his and when he stood barely inches away there was nothing she could do to stop the trembling of her lips nor the single tear that spilled and ran slowly down her cheek. Surely she wasn't going to cry—that would give him the utmost satisfaction.

'*Por Dios*,' he cursed softly. 'I am sorely tempted to give you the beating you deserve.' He gazed down into her eyes for seemingly endless seconds before letting the shoe fall from his hand. 'Try my patience on one more occasion, *mi mujer*, and you will indeed weep,' he threatened darkly, and his eyes swept her from head to toe with slow deliberation. 'There are more ways than one to deal with a recalcitrant wife.'

His meaning was unmistakable, and Terese suppressed an involuntary shiver of apprehension. She held her breath as he turned away and gave a silent sigh of relief as he strode into his dressing-room. Wearily she sat down on the edge of the bed, suddenly too tired to be bothered getting undressed. The very thought of discarding clothes for silk pyjamas disturbed her senses more than she was prepared to admit, and she felt in desperate need of a friendly sympathetic shoulder to which she could cling and receive a measure of understanding. But there was no one she could confide in, for none of her friends would really believe she had chosen against all her better instincts to marry a man she hated. It had to be hate, this wild curling sensation that began whenever he touched her. To think of it as any other emotion was ridiculous.

A slight sound made her look up, and there was no time to mask the aching emotion-filled expression in her eyes before she stood swiftly to her feet and moved towards her dressing-room.

'Terese.'

The sound of Manuel's voice brought her to a halt, but she couldn't turn and face him.

'You will give me the card with the address of the garage,' he commanded quietly, and she could ascertain little from the tone of his voice. 'Until your car is roadworthy, Santanas will transport both you and your stepfather wherever you wish to go.'

'Thank you, but——'

'There will be no *but*, Terese,' he voiced hardily, and she flinched inwardly at his implacability.

'I'll get the card from my bag,' she said shakily as she stepped into her dressing-room. Quickly she found what she wanted, and when she turned round he was standing directly in front of her. The navy towelling robe accentuated the natural olive texture of his skin, and there were dark curling hairs on his chest where the robe parted. He appeared dynamically masculine, and she doubted he wore anything beneath the robe, for he displayed no embarrassment at sleeping totally unadorned beneath the bedcovers.

Silently she handed him the card and became suddenly panic-stricken as he reached out to grasp her shoulders. 'Please let me get changed,' she pleaded desperately in an attempt to escape him, but already one hand tangled the hair at her nape while the other cupped her chin and tilted it so that she had to meet his gaze.

'You have no need to be so afraid of me, *querida*,' he murmured gently as his lips brushed a fleeting caress against the corner of her mouth.

'It's not you I'm afraid of,' she longed to cry out in protest, hardly aware of anything coherent as he deliberately sought to bring alive the sensual flame deep within her. To remain cool and indifferent was becoming increasingly difficult, and perhaps she was foolish to imagine she might win any battles against him this way.

'I'm a traitor to myself,' she echoed silently a long time afterwards as she lay listening to his deep rhythmic breathing. An outflung arm imprisoned her close to his side, and even in sleep his hold was possessive.

She must have slept, for there were dreams chasing her subconscious mind in a glorious kaleidoscope where segments revealed no logical sequence, but in each stood the shadowy figure of a man. He came closer and closer towards her until he was within touching distance, and she stood still, unable to move away as she waited to see the face emerge from the shadows. He was calling her name, softly at first, then with an increasing urgency, and suddenly his face was revealed in a pool of light and she cried out in fright.

'Terese! *Madre de Dios*—wake up, child!' Manuel's voice penetrated the depths of her mind, and she blinked up at him as he leaned over her. The bed-lamp was alight and there was a feeling of unreality pervading the room.

'I was dreaming,' she offered abstractly, her eyes wide and luminous as she gazed up at him.

'That is an understatement,' Manuel said dryly as he lifted a few strands of long hair that lay across her cheek and placed them against the pillow.

'What time is it?'

'Almost four o'clock,' he answered after a brief glance at his watch on the bedside table. 'Do you wish to talk about that nightmarish bogy of yours—or perhaps his name is Manuel?' There was a certain wryness in his tone as he raked her features.

She held his gaze steadily. 'I woke just as his face emerged from the shadows. I wasn't afraid—I just couldn't move away.'

'Your cry at the sight of my face was scarcely one of relief.'

'I would probably have cried out no matter who woke me,' she offered quietly. 'I'm not accustomed to sharing a room with anyone—much less a bed.'

'Are you advocating separate beds so early in our marriage?' he slanted quizzically, and his lips curved into a smile as a blush coloured her cheeks.

Vexed by his ability to affect her emotions, Terese turned away and determinedly plumped her pillow, refusing to answer him.

A light chuckle escaped his throat as he switched off the lamp and settled down close beside her. '*Buenas noches*, Terese Delgado.'

'*Buenos dias*, Manuel Sebastian Rafael Delgado,' she corrected with a touch of wry impudence.

CHAPTER FIVE

THROUGHOUT breakfast next morning Terese toyed with the food on her plate eating little, and finally settled for a slice of toast as she drank her coffee. Just how she could broach the subject of her intention to go out with Meg this evening was becoming more difficult with every passing minute. The ideal solution was to come right out with it and reason with him, but Manuel was not likely to be reasonable. In fact the more she thought about it, the more certain she became that he would refuse.

'There is something on your mind?'

She cast him a startled glance and at the intentness of his gaze steadied her coffee cup with both hands. He was far too discerning for her peace of mind!

'Should there be?' she countered lightly, and veiled her eyes so that he couldn't read their expression.

'I have the distinct impression you are planning something that would not meet with my approval,' Manuel drawled sardonically.

'You've made it abundantly clear I must obey your every command,' she stated sweetly. 'The consequences of not doing so have been painfully demonstrated.'

His dark eyes flicked over her mobile features and narrowed fractionally. 'I have a business dinner to attend this evening, and will therefore not be home until late.'

Elation began to stir inside her at this information. With an attempt to keep the query casual she enquired tentatively, 'How late do you think you will be?'

'I will not expect you to wait up for me, *mi esposa*,' he returned with wry cynicism.

'I had no intention of doing so,' she assured sedately, watching as he folded his table napkin and rose to his feet.

'Take care, *mi mujer*, of that foolish tongue. Already you have felt the heat of my anger—I would not advise the folly of doing so again.'

'Go to work, Manuel, and leave me in peace,' she said warily.

'*Adios*,' he saluted mockingly. 'Until tonight.'

'I shall probably be asleep,' Terese retorted uncharitably.

'Then I shall wake you,' he replied imperturbably.

Terese didn't answer—she felt the words would have choked in her throat. When he had gone she poured another cup of coffee and sipped it meditatively as she pondered the best strategy with which to acquaint Sofia that she also would not be in for dinner this evening. It was unlikely Manuel would telephone through the day, but it was a possibility that had to be considered and she daren't risk either Sofia or Santanas telling him that she intended going out for the evening. Much better to leave it until Santanas brought her back from visiting Steve this afternoon.

'You have finished, *señora*?'

Terese looked up into Sofia's kindly face and smiled. 'Thank you, Sofia—yes.'

'May I ask at what time you wish to leave this morning?'

'You can tell Santanas that nine o'clock will be fine, if that's convenient with him. As my husband'—that was only the second time she had openly referred to Manuel as her husband, and the words almost choked her—'won't be dining at home tonight, I'll just have something light on a tray in the *sala*.'

Sofia nodded and murmured in agreement as she collected dishes from the table.

With luck Manuel would be none the wiser that she had gone out until she told him tomorrow at breakfast. He was bound to be cross—cross was far too mild a word, he'd be incredibly furious, of that she was positive! However, she would weather that particular storm when it came.

Meg was delighted when Terese telephoned two hours later to tell her that she would be able to come, after all. Deciding she might as well do the thing properly, she readily agreed to meet Meg at a city restaurant for dinner before going on to the theatre. Even then a niggling feeling of guilt began to gnaw at her conscience, and twice during the day Steve cast her a probing glance and asked if something was troubling her—but she shook her head and smiled, and pointed to something of scenic interest as Santanas directed the Daimler smoothly along the Princes highway towards Geelong.

One might almost suppose there was a mission of ill-intent in view, Terese grimaced somewhat wryly when Santanas brought the car to a halt outside the Toorak residence in the late afternoon. Although he was carefully polite, Santanas' tone indicated definite disapproval of the Señora's intention to dine out alone.

'I shan't be dining alone, Santanas,' she corrected hurriedly. 'If you could drive me into the city in'— she spared a quick glance at her wristwatch—'about an hour's time, I'll let Sofia know that I won't be in to dinner. My friend has a car and she'll probably bring me home, so there will be no necessity for you to collect me.'

'Si, señora.'

'Well, Terese Delgado,' a tiny voice whispered inside

her brain, 'you seem bent on doing something that will inevitably bring unpleasant repercussions of a kind you'd be wise to avoid.' But it was too late now, and why, oh, why did she have to feel so guilty—almost as if she were committing a crime!

'What are you going to choose, Terese?'

Terese looked across the top of the menu at Meg's pleasant features and smiled engagingly. 'We've plenty of time—let's have a little from each course. My treat —I insist.'

'Terese——' Meg began protestingly, then she suddenly smiled. 'Why not? I temporarily forgot that you're now a wealthy woman.' Her impudence was imparted in a humorous vein. 'You can tell me what manner of man he is—I still can't believe it! Manuel Delgado—one of the most eligible bachelors in Melbourne, and my best friend manages to snare him into matrimony,' Meg paused mockingly. 'Tell me the secret of your success, *please?*'

'If I told you, you wouldn't believe me,' Terese said calmly.

'Uh-huh—she's not about to divulge anything,' Meg sighed resignedly as she scrutinised the wine list. 'Let's have something out of the ordinary by way of a celebration. It's not every day I get to dine in such exalted company!'

'Exalted——!'

'Relax, dear Terese,' Meg interrupted impishly. 'I'm well aware you're no snob. Millionaire's wife you may be, but to you I doubt his wealth is of much importance.'

'Tell me how things are at the hospital,' she bade determinedly in an effort to change the topic of conversation.

Meg shot her a slightly puzzled glance. 'A few of the

children have been asking after you, of course, and the new junior nurse on your ward is not going to make it to the end of her training. Honestly, do you know what she managed to do yesterday?' Meg shook her head incredulously, and for the next half an hour they became engrossed in hospital gossip.

It was just as the waiter was serving the main course that Meg caught her breath and touched Terese's arm.

'That man who has just come in—I'm almost sure it's your husband.'

Terese's eyes flew to the entrance foyer and she couldn't suppress the startled gasp that escaped her lips. There was no mistaking the identity of that tall dark-haired figure as he stood in conversation with the head waiter. With fearful fascination she saw him nod an acknowledgment and begin making his way towards their table.

'*Buenas tardes.*' Manuel's voice was a deep drawl and his eyes held a hint of mockery as he voiced the greeting and slipped into the chair the waiter held out for him. There followed a brief consultation as he placed an order and requested more wine, then with complete ease he took Terese's hand and raised it to his lips. 'My business colleague unfortunately had to postpone his dinner engagement this evening.' His eyes were dark and inscrutable as they met hers, but his very calm held a warning of anger. 'I did not imagine you would object to my joining both you and your friend.' He smiled at Meg, who promptly proceeded to assure him most earnestly that they didn't mind in the least.

Terese hastily swallowed as Manuel sent her a questioning look. 'Meg is a close friend—we both worked at the same hospital,' she explained quickly. 'Meg Cameron—my husband, Manuel.'

Manuel's smile was charming as was his manner, and it became rapidly evident that Meg was smitten. She was bright and amusing, and she more than made up for Terese's lack of conversation throughout the meal.

'Perhaps our theatre tickets could be exchanged,' Meg suggested warmly. 'Terese did particularly want to see the show,' she turned to Manuel with this information. 'We've had the tickets for several weeks.'

'If I could have the tickets, I will endeavour to arrange three seats together for this evening's performance,' he declared smoothly.

'You'll come with us?' Terese couldn't help the incredulous query.

'We'd be delighted,' Meg's eyes glowed enthusiastically, and with a slight nod Manuel stood to his feet voicing his intention to make enquiries via the telephone in the lobby.

'I hope he can manage it,' Meg enthused. 'He's even more attractive in the flesh—photographs don't really do him justice. He obviously adores you.'

Oh, Meg, Terese mentally shook her head, if you only knew!

In a short space of time Manuel returned to the table and confirmed that he had been successful—there had been little trouble in exchanging the tickets, and he proceeded to order coffee with every evidence of satisfaction. Only Terese saw that his smile didn't quite reach his eyes, and the anger beneath the surface of his control.

On reflection, it would have been an enjoyable evening if she hadn't been in a state of suspended trepidation. The live performance at the theatre was everything the advertisements had declared it to be, and afterwards Manuel seemed inclined to continue playing the part of genial host for he advocated supper, over which he seemed to be in no hurry to finish.

Inevitably it came time to leave, and after seeing Meg safely to her car and on her way, Manuel took Terese's arm and led her the short distance to the Mercedes-Benz.

Seated inside, she sat perfectly still and offered nary a word as he slid in beside her and set the car in motion. The drive home was achieved in total silence, and even after the car had been garaged and they entered the house still not a word passed between them.

Terese felt as if a time-fuse was set on his anger and that any moment it would explode. Inside their bedroom she turned round to face him defiantly.

'Whatever it is you intend doing to me, at least get it over and done with.' Even so, she couldn't prevent the slight quiver in her voice.

'All evening you have been waiting for the moment I will pounce,' he evinced sardonically. 'Tell me—was it your intention to keep me in ignorance of this escapade?'

'If you hadn't have been dining out tonight, I would have told Meg I couldn't go,' she declared indignantly. 'But when I learned you weren't going to be home until late, I decided to meet Meg and tell you tomorrow.'

'Naturally in the hope that you would arrive home before I did.' He paused speculatively. 'Surely you must have had some idea as to the extent of my anger had I arrived home first?'

'I expected you to be angry—yes.'

'It is as well Santanas drove you directly to the restaurant and therefore I knew where to find you.'

'Oh, really, Manuel!' she exclaimed bitterly. 'I am an individualistic human being, and to me you are nothing less than an egotistical tyrant!'

'Careful, my little cat,' he warned, and his eyes gleamed hard and cold.

'Do you know how *guilty* I've felt all day?' she rushed on heedlessly. 'It wasn't as if—as if I was going out with another man. And yet I felt as if I were committing a crime.' She was thoroughly vexed by now. 'I suppose if you had dined with Nadine Norcroft I would have been expected to turn a blind eye!'

'Poor *niña*—jealous?'

At the wry amusement in his voice she clenched a fist and swung it furiously in a swift-moving arc towards that mocking mouth, only to have it halted midway.

'Oh no, my beautiful cat, that you will not do,' he drawled deliberately as he pulled her close against his hard lean frame.

'Punishment, Manuel?' Terese threw at him angrily. 'I already have more bruises than I can count.'

For one heart-stopping moment she thought he meant to slap her and she closed her eyes in defence of his assault. It never came, and seconds later he roughly put her aside and strode into his dressing-room.

Shakily she moved across the room, undressing and showering with undue haste so that she could slip between the bedcovers before he did. If she hadn't still been harbouring anger against him she might have seen the humour in them both re-entering the bedroom simultaneously to slip beneath the bedcovers within seconds of each other.

In the darkness he reached for her, moulding her pliant young body to the muscular hardness of his own, his lips wreaking havoc to her outraged senses in a manner that left her in no doubt of his intent to punish, and it was only after a seemingly interminable length of time that he relented. He claimed her then, with a mastery that sent her arms clinging to him with such wanton abandon she wept silent tears of shame long after he gently set her from him.

During the following few days Terese began to relax her guard a little. Santanas proved an excellent chauffeur, and Steve enjoyed the luxury of being driven in ultimate comfort. On Tuesday they drove through Bacchus Marsh and Ballan to Ballarat, and on Wednesday the Daimler transported them via the Bass highway to Cowes. They lunched in style each day, insisting Santanas join them, and the weather held, although it was bitterly cold whenever they stepped out from the warmth of the heated car. Perhaps it was at Manuel's instigation that Sofia packed a hamper each day with flasks of coffee and an assortment of cakes and sandwiches for morning and afternoon tea at wherever they chose to halt.

Steve declined to visit friends en route, and seemed to want only the beauty of the countryside and Terese's company. If Santanas deduced anything from their conversation it could only have evoked sympathy, for whatever his personal thoughts regarding his employer's sudden marriage to none other than the stepdaughter of the man responsible for the tragic accident four weeks ago, it was obvious that he had taken it upon himself to become both friend and companion. Steve reminisced endlessly, bringing tears of laughter tinged with sadness, and although Terese's Mini was delivered late Wednesday afternoon after a complete mechanical overhaul there was no mention of it being used and Santanas' services dispensed with.

The evenings were relatively quiet as they usually dined together alone, after which Manuel would inevitably retire to his study and Terese either viewed television or listened to selected record albums on the stereo. On Wednesday evening he joined her in the *sala* as she was about to go upstairs to bed, and the following evening she was already in bed and on the verge of sleep when he entered their room.

On Friday evening they were to attend a prestigious charity dinner at one of Melbourne's exclusive restaurants, and Terese's excitement was pure feminine reaction at having selected a truly beautiful evening-gown and utilising Manuel's credit card with disgraceful disregard. Of soft filamel sky-blue jersey with deep flounces, it clung to her slender curves and flared gracefully down to her toes. It was perfect, although the amount on the price-tag was staggering! She bought delicate silver-strapped evening sandals and a silver evening bag, and impulsively purchased a complete range of new make-up as well. True, she did experience a slight qualm at shamelessly spending so much money, but Manuel could well afford it. A tiny voice inside her head sparked vengefully alive and prompted her into assuming a devil-may-care attitude towards making such free use of his charge account. The more she thought about it the more justified she felt. Manuel would find the acquisition of a wife could prove expensive!

Santanas relieved her of most of the parcels when she reached the car, and as they drove out of the inner city through St Kilda Terese gazed at the wide tree-lined streets in silence. There was a great deal of traffic and the trams were crammed to capacity with city commuters homeward bound after work. The grey skies above were rapidly darkening into nightfall and long slashes of rain began to assault the car, increasing rapidly into a major downpour which made visibility difficult and driving hazardous.

There was barely time to unpack all her purchases before she heard Manuel enter their room, and she quickly slipped into the bathroom and turned on the shower. She would have loved the luxury of a lazy soak in the bath with lots of essence-scented hot water, but there wasn't time.

There was no doubt the evening gown was worth every cent, and although Terese hadn't bought it with the intention of seeking Manuel's admiration, nevertheless she felt pleased when he voiced his approval.

'Thank you,' she smiled, and took in his appearance with a quick glance. In a black suit with crisp white linen he presented an awesome figure and her heart gave a crazy lurch as it began to thud against her ribs. 'You don't look too bad yourself,' she managed evenly.

His eyebrows rose quizzically and an amused smile curved his lips. '*Gracias, mi mujer*,' he acknowledged dryly.

Terese picked up her coat and masked her confusion as he took it from her hands and held it out so that she could slip her arms into its sleeves. For the sake of something to say she uttered the first thing that came into her head.

'What time do you call for Isabella tomorrow morning? Have you any plans for the weekend?'

'We will collect her at nine and drive down to the stud farm at Danenong where we will all spend the weekend.'

'Oh,' she shot him a puzzled look. 'What kind of stud farm?'

'Racehorses—I breed and sell them as yearlings,' he informed her laconically. 'A manager lives on the property and I endeavour to spend as many weekends there as possible. Fortunately Isabella has a passion for horses—she has her own pony and has a riding lesson whenever we stay there. Do you ride?'

Terese made a wry grimace. Ride? The closest she had ever come to a horse was on the other side of the fence at a friend's farm further up-State. 'No,' she answered cautiously as she preceded him into the corridor.

'That is something we will remedy—beginning to-morrow,' he declared smoothly.

'I'd much prefer to watch Isabella,' Terese vouched steadily. To have Manuel become her riding instructor was something she would prefer to avoid.

'It is time to leave,' he said enigmatically.

And that took care of that, Terese thought brood-ingly, sure that tomorrow would bring her into contact with a horse. Steadily and surely Manuel was emerging the victor as he imposed his authority, and she felt the familiar rankling of resentment against him.

The dinner was an unqualified success. The food and wine were superb, and the pop group of musicians played non-stop through the entire evening, alternating be-tween the slow country-and-western type of music to out-and-out rock. The women were all dressed in their finest, and the men wore dark suits and dress-shirts. Some of Melbourne's wealthiest patrons were present, and Terese espied Nadine Norcroft within the first few minutes of their arrival. She sat opposite at the same table and Terese was aware of her scrutiny throughout the meal.

It became obvious that Manuel was held in high re-gard, and as his wife Terese was aware of a certain amount of speculation. He was faultlessly courteous and attentive without carrying it to the extreme, and not one person present could have guessed he was other than a devoted husband. True, he appeared faintly cynical—

even bored by the obviously elite array of guests. Terese had the oddest feeling that he would much preferred to have impersonally donated a cheque through the mail thus enabling him to escape the social formalities.

The conversation at their table was little more than the polite social chatter that is engaged upon at such functions, and by the time the main course had been served Terese was beginning to become irritated by Nadine's obvious attempts to monopolise Manuel's attention. She spoke to him almost exclusively and her eyes were openly seducing to a point where it was becoming embarrassing.

'I must ask how you met Manuel—and where?' Nadine's voice tinkled as with a soft laugh she shifted her attention to Terese.

'Wouldn't you just love to scratch my eyes out?' Terese thought wryly, sensing the other woman's desire to begin a sophisticated verbal attack. She met the barely veiled enmity in Nadine's eyes and summoned a smile to her lips. 'Does it matter?'

A brittle laugh escaped Nadine's lips as she made a deliberate moue. 'Of course, darling. We're utterly fascinated by your victory. Many have tried, believe me.'

'I don't doubt it,' Terese replied albeit sweetly, and she was intensely aware of Manuel's dark sardonic gaze.

'Your dear little niece has gained a cute playmate, Manuel,' Nadine drawled provocatively. 'Where did you find her?'

Terese inwardly fumed at the woman's sarcasm and her eyes flashed as she realised Manuel was enjoying their barbed exchange.

'Quite literally on my doorstep,' Manuel enlightened musingly. 'Breathing fire and fury like a miniature dragon.'

Nadine's eyebrows rose a fraction. 'Really? Manuel, I suspect you are being deliberately facetious,' she protested and assumed a coy expression.

'Not at all.' He sounded bored and faintly cynical. Turning to Terese, he lifted a hand to tuck back a few stray strands of her hair and then let the tips of his fingers trail gently across her cheek. 'Dance with me, *amada*.'

Terese felt her stomach curl at the sensuality in his softly-voiced command. She would dearly have liked to refuse, but the challenging glint in his eyes was sufficient deterrent. Silently she followed him on to the dance floor and was enfolded against his hard frame in a manner that was hardly conventional.

'Lift your arms and clasp your hands behind my neck,' he bade her quietly.

'Why are you behaving like this?' Terese asked in a strangled voice a few minutes later as she felt his lips brush against her temple. 'Surely it isn't necessary to appear so convincing?' The strangest feeling was stealing over her, rendering her limbs boneless and jelly-like.

'Must you have a reason?'

Terese refrained from answering. They moved slowly among the mingling couples on the floor, neither of them attempting to make further conversation, and she drew a silent sigh of relief when the music changed tempo and he led her back to their table.

'I presume you worked for Manuel in some capacity?'

Terese looked across the table at Nadine Norcroft and her dislike of the woman increased measurably. She was persistent and deadly over obtaining her objective—that objective being Manuel Sebastian Rafael Delgado!

'You presume wrong,' she answered calmly enough.

Nadine's eyes narrowed and her fingers tightened

95

about the delicate stem of her wine-glass. 'I haven't seen you at any of the many social functions Manuel has attended over the past few months,' she observed derogatorily.

Terese drew a deep breath and expelled it slowly. 'Manuel has already explained how we met.'

Nadine's eyebrows rose delicately. 'You simply presented yourself at his door? Nothing like the direct approach, darling,' she drawled disparagingly.

'I'm so glad you agree,' Terese replied sweetly.

'You won't object if I commandeer your husband for a dance?' Nadine arched her brows and threw a stunning smile towards Manuel.

'Sorry, Nadine,' he declined without any semblance of regret, and his expression assumed that of bored distaste when Nadine laughed bitterly.

'Such a pity to waste your talents, Manuel,' she accorded viciously.

'Waste?' he drawled cynically, and his eyes became dark and cold. 'I think not.'

'I'm a sore loser, darling. Didn't you know?'

Manuel threw a chilling look in her direction. 'I wasn't aware that you had been a contender,' he averred hardily.

Terese felt sickened. She needed to get away from this invidious scene and Nadine's spitefully barbed inneundoes. 'I'd like to leave,' she said quietly and distinctly, uncaring whether Manuel accompanied her or not.

Nadine laughed mockingly. 'Can't take it, sweetie?'

'I won't sit here and be humiliated, if that's what you mean,' she began with quiet conviction. 'And I really don't care what your affair with my husband amounted to, Nadine,' she said evenly, standing to her feet. 'Contrary to your conjecture, Manuel swept me into marriage before I had time to draw breath!'

'*Brava!*' Manuel's soft chuckle rippled with wry amusement as he rose to his feet and directed a curt bow towards Nadine. '*Adios.*' He took Terese's elbow in a firm grasp and led the way through the mingling guests to the main entrance.

Terese didn't say a word in the car, and only when they were home did she voice her thoughts. 'Perhaps you will tell me how many other women I can expect to do verbal battle with?'

His light laugh was her undoing and she rounded on him in utter fury.

'You actually enjoyed it, didn't you? There was a certain amount of sadistic pleasure—oh, I hate you! I *hate* you!' she cried wrathfully.

'Ah, *querida*, that is not so,' he shrugged lightly, and there was amusement lurking in the depths of his eyes which only served to increase her anger.

'I am not your darling—I never will be anything to you other than—than an object with whom you can fulfil your insatiable desires,' she threw at him furiously, and then to her complete and utter consternation she burst into tears.

Terese turned and ran, not even seeing where she ran in her haste to escape. Halfway up the stairs she tripped on the hem of her long evening gown and fell on to her hands and knees. With an anguished sob she scrambled to her feet as she caught sight of Manuel immediately behind and wrenched away as he caught and lifted her effortlessly.

'Leave me alone!' She struggled hopelessly as he swung her over one shoulder, and she beat clenched fists against his broad back all the way to their bedroom.

'*Madre mia*—that is enough!'

The tone of his voice effectively stilled her flailing arms and silent tears of shame rolled down her cheeks as he released his hold and set her on her feet.

'*Ay-ay-ay*—such fury!' His dark gleaming eyes raked mercilessly, missing nothing, and there was a momentary flaring of tenderness in his expression as he pushed her tumbled hair back from her face. 'Believe me, I had no prior knowledge that Nadine Norcroft would be sharing our table.' Lightly he brushed his fingers across her cheeks and swore beneath his breath as two large tears slowly rolled down to her chin.

'You were cruel—so deliberately cruel to her,' Terese said abstractly, and was unable to meet his eyes.

Manuel muffled a stream of explicit Spanish epithets. 'You sympathise with such a woman?' he queried a trifle harshly.

'She loves you,' Terese offered slowly.

'*Love?*' he expostulated grimly, and his hands moved to grasp her shoulders. 'You don't know what you're talking about, child. Sex—physical lust,' he elaborated brutally. 'Nadine is a sophisticated social butterfly who slips in and out of as many silken beds as she can manage, with intent to add as many gifts of jewellery or whatever to her considerable collection.' He went on to state sardonically, 'Nadine discovered *love* and dispensed it from the probable age of sixteen!'

'I think you're perfectly horrid,' Terese whispered with shocked incredulity.

'And you, *mi esposa*, are about as sophisticated as a babe in arms,' he replied dryly.

'*Gracias*,' she retorted perversely.

Hard fingers gripped her chin and forced it high so

that she had to meet his dark gaze. 'That was intended as a compliment, not a condemnation.'

'Some compliment,' she muttered, her eyes still stormy.

'Poor *niña*,' Manuel drawled quizzically, and fastened his mouth to hers, deliberately teasing her lips with his own before seeking the soft hollows at the base of her throat.

'Stop trying to—to seduce me,' she protested vexedly as she endeavoured to escape from his arms and the sensual touch of his lips.

'Why struggle, *querida*? You are not as averse to my lovemaking as you would pretend.'

Terese forced scorn into her voice, hating the warm flood of pink she knew to be colouring her cheeks. 'I find your touch utterly loathsome!'

'Then you will no doubt welcome my absence,' he remarked wryly.

'You're going away?' she queried tentatively after a measurable silence.

'I fly to Adelaide early Monday morning on business.'

'Oh,' she uttered slowly, unsure of her emotions. 'How long will you be away?'

'Four—five days.'

'I'll go home.' To her surprise she had spoken the words aloud.

'*Home?* Are you not forgetting that this is now your home?' There was a degree of anger lurking in his eyes which Terese chose to ignore.

'I'll be spending each day with Steve,' she voiced reasonably. 'As you won't be here, why shouldn't I stay?'

'You are my wife,' Manuel stated hardily. 'And as such

your place is in my home.'

Terese felt the anger within her begin to rise. 'You refuse to let me go?'

'If you do not give me your word that you will return here each evening, you will accompany me to Adelaide.'

She stared at him incredulously. 'Why? What possible difference can it make?'

'Do I have your word?' he countered smoothly.

'No,' she glared resentfully. 'I'm not a child to be given orders as to what I can or can't do!'

His eyes flicked over her expressively. 'Your behaviour is very much that of a child.'

'Oh, naturally,' she agreed bitterly. 'If I were more *sophisticated* I would employ feminine wiles to achieve my own ends.'

'Perhaps you would care to demonstrate such "feminine wiles"?' Manuel broached with interest, and his eyes gleamed devilishly.

'I'd die first!'

'Poor *niña*,' he clicked his teeth and amusement twisted the corners of his mouth into a slight smile. 'Come to bed.' He lifted a hand and lightly caressed her cheek.

'I don't want to go to bed,' Terese bit out peevishly as she met his frankly sensuous eyes, and she turned her head aside in an effort to avoid his lips. She cried out as his hand gripped the back of her neck and a silent moan of entreaty escaped her lips as his mouth found hers with bruising intensity.

When at last he lifted his head she was a quivering mass of nerves and ached with treacherous desire.

'Do you not?' His voiced query was faintly teasing, and when she stood silent within the circle of his arms he bent down to bestow a kiss to each of her eyelids in turn. 'Am I so hateful, *querida*?'

'Some of the time, yes,' Terese admitted honestly, and ventured an expressive sigh as she looked up at him. 'I think you find my lack of experience amusing.'

Manuel smiled a little and gently shook her. 'Your "lack of experience", as you so delicately phrase it, I find wholly delightful.' He probed the hollows at the base of her throat with his thumb, fully aware of the havoc his touch evoked. 'You are proving an apt pupil, my little cat.'

She felt the warm rush of colour to her face and opened her mouth to begin a verbal attack. 'Oh——' she raised angry eyes as he effectively stilled her words by pressing her lips closed with a lean finger.

'No,' he mocked softly, shaking his head. 'Do you imagine I am unaware of your response simply because in the dark your expression is elusive?'

Terese felt her lips tremble as she recalled all too vividly the abandoned way in which she had clung to him on each and every one of those occasions, and at that moment she hated him almost as much as she hated herself.

'The weekend will prove a welcome diversion, will it not? For Isabella's benefit we must put forth an image of mutual contentment, and I shall be away for much of next week. Who knows,' he mused lightly, 'perhaps you will discover you miss your "some-of-the-time-hateful" Spanish *esposo*, hmmn?'

'That would be hoping for the impossible,' she retorted quickly, and tried to ignore the deep curling sensation that began deep within her and rapidly encompassed her being, rendering her weak-willed and

101

totally malleable as he drew her to him. She felt his hands move over her hips, pressing her close until she was wholly aware of his needs, and she was scarcely conscious of being gently divested of every last vestige of clothing before he drew her down on to the silk-sheeted bed.

CHAPTER SIX

ISABELLA greeted both Terese and Manuel with an enthusiasm Terese found oddly touching when they called to collect the little girl from the convent next morning. During the drive to Dandenong they were re-galed with Isabella's excited chattering of the week's events, and on arriving at the stud farm she leaned forward to bestow a kiss to each of their cheeks in turn before giving a contented sigh.

'Oh, Tio Manuel, I do love coming here,' Isabella vouchsafed eagerly. 'Don't you think it's a wonderful place, Terese? Mr and Mrs Dalbeth live in that house down there, and the stables are not far away.' She skip-ped up and down as Manuel took their overnight bags and Isabella's suitcase from the boot of the Mercedes-Benz.

Terese looked about with interest. The house was built of dark grey stone pointed with white cement, and set low on the ground. The windows were multi-paned and showed yards of decoratively gathered white frilled curtains behind the sparkling glass.

They entered via a side verandah into an enormous kitchen and it became immediately apparent that there was central heating installed throughout as the house was comfortingly warm. Isabella skipped after Manuel and Terese followed behind them, frankly delighted with everything she saw. There was a formal dining-room, a large lounge, four bedrooms—all of which had adjoining bathrooms, a family room almost as large as the lounge, and a study. Somehow the house seemed to exude a feeling of cosy informality, a warmth that spelled 'home' with loving care.

'It's beautiful!' Terese enthused spontaneously to Manuel as she began unpacking their overnight bags. 'I could live here.'

'I'm pleased it meets with your approval,' he acknowledged somewhat mockingly as he noted her glowing expression.

'The Toorak—mansion,' Terese wrinkled her nose a little, 'well, it's superbly elegant and perfect for entertaining. But this—this is home—a family kind of home,' she elaborated.

'The kind of home that should be filled with several children, *si*?'

'Children would make it complete, yes,' Terese answered briefly, not daring to look at him. Children— their children, more particularly *his* children, wasn't a thought she wanted to pursue in depth.

'Why are you talking about children? Are you going to have a baby, Terese?' Isabella questioned inquisitively from her perched position on the edge of the large double-bed.

'Such things take time, *pequeña*,' Manuel drawled laconically as he swung the child high into his arms. 'Already we have made a start—with you, have we not?'

'*Si*,' Isabella giggled delightedly as she sat astride Manuel's powerful shoulders and clung to his thick dark

103

hair with both hands. 'It takes nine months for humans to get babies and more than a year for elephants,' she declared knowledgeably. 'Sister Ignacia told us all about it.'

'Three cheers for Sister Ignacia,' Terese muttered beneath her breath, then cast Isabella a mischievous smile in an attempt to cover up her own embarrassment. 'Thank goodness I'm not an elephant! Although perhaps I might resemble a tiny elephant when the baby is almost due to be born!'

'Then Tio Manuel and I will look after you and make sure you have lots of rest,' the little imp declared earnestly. 'Oh, hurry up and become *encinta*, Terese. You must talk to Tio Manuel about making babies. Mustn't she?' Isabella besought her uncle, who had begun to chuckle deep in the back of his throat as he caught Terese's startled expression.

'I think all this talk of babies is making Terese shy, *pequeña*. See how she blushes?'

'Why do you go pink, Terese? Do you not wish to make babies with Tio Manuel?'

'Just wait until I get you alone, Manuel Delgado!' Terese vowed silently. 'Sí, Isabella, but Tio Manuel is one *macho hombre*, to whom I have been married for just one week,' she managed evenly.

Manuel lifted Isabella down and stood her gently on her feet. 'Mr Dalbeth will have seen us arrive, and he will expect you at any moment to pay a visit to Karina in her stall. Run along while I show Terese where everything is kept in the kitchen, then we will join you down at the stables, *sí*?' He tweaked her ear and smiled indulgently as she blew them both a kiss and ran from the room.

'So I am one *macho hombre*, am I, *mi esposa*?' he

queried softly, and his dark eyes were agleam with devilish laughter.

Terese deigned not to answer as she shot him an eloquent glance before turning away to stow the now-empty overnight bags at the bottom of the wardrobe. 'You were going to show me the kitchen,' she stated coolly.

'Ah, yes,' he acknowledged mockingly. 'Food—you can cook, I presume? In the past I have cooked lunch and Mrs Dalbeth has despatched sufficient for our evening meal, but now I have acquired a wife ...' he allowed his voice to trail off expressively.

'*You* have cooked meals?' Terese couldn't help her astonishment.

'I am not incapable of such things,' Manuel drawled cynically. 'You disbelieve me?'

'If you say it is so, then I suppose you can. Somehow I just can't imagine you being useful in a kitchen.' She stifled a grin, but not quick enough.

'Just for that, *I* will cook the lunch today. Your culinary efforts can wait until this evening. Agreed?'

Terese preceded him into the hallway and moved quickly towards the back door. 'Why not?'

Isabella was engaged in a one-sided conversation with her pony when they arrived at the stables and it was obvious both child and animal shared an idolatory rapport.

'Isn't she just simply beautiful?' Isabella sought of Terese. 'She is my very own. Tio Manuel bought her for me.'

'She's lovely,' Terese agreed affectionately. 'Are you going to show me how well you ride?'

'After lunch,' Manuel promised with a smile as he stroked a hand down the animal's neck. 'Now that you

105

have renewed your acquaintance with Karina, we will introduce Terese to Mr and Mrs Dalbeth, *si?*'

Terese tried to extricate her hand as he clasped it firmly within his own, but her furtive efforts were in vain, and the dark glance he slanted down at her was sufficient a warning not to struggle. There was nothing for it but to suffer his touch, and she endeavoured to sweep aside the deep frustration his presence seemed to cause.

Mrs Dalbeth had laid out morning tea, and the aroma of freshly baked scones and percolated coffee was genuinely welcome. A homely soul, middle-aged and comfortably plump, it was easy to see she adored Isabella and sanctioned Manuel's marriage with a wholeheartedness that was almost embarrassing.

It was almost an hour before they took their leave and wandered slowly back towards the grey stone house close to the road. The sun was bravely vying with the clouds for supremacy in an indifferent sky, the wind chill as it whipped gently at her hair to send strands flying about her shoulders and on to her face. The grass was lushly green from the winter's rain and tall beech trees lined the boundaries, providing partial shelter and privacy from neighbouring properties. If Manuel's sleek Mercedes-Benz had not been visible the setting could easily have belonged to an earlier pioneer era.

'You will both make ready the table while I attend to the stove, *si?*' Manuel delivered briskly as they stepped into the kitchen. 'Then Terese can explore the deep-freezer and the contents of the cupboards in an attempt to decide what she will serve us for dinner.'

'Oh, lovely!' Isabella smiled engagingly from her uncle to Terese. 'Tio Manuel isn't very good at puddings, Terese.'

'Men never are,' Terese grinned towards the little girl. 'Which pudding do you like best?'.

'Those lovely upside-down ones with lots of hot golden syrup running all over, and lashings of whipped cream,' Isabella said instantly.

'You shall have it,' Terese promised gaily, safe in the knowledge that the dessert was one of her specialities. With pasta to begin the meal, she decided after an inspection of the selection of food available, and a chicken casserole to follow.

Manuel concocted tasty *tortillas* that held mushrooms, onions and bacon, and served grilled steaks and a salad with the ease of a man who had had much practice, and Terese couldn't help but feel surprised that he should choose to cook meals when it would have been all too simple to bring Santanas and Sofia with them for the weekend.

'Coffee?'

Terese started visibly at the sound of her husband's voice, and her eyes caught the slight mockery evident in his dark gaze as she inclined her head in assent.

'When you have loaded the dishwasher we will get changed and I will give you both your riding lesson,' Manuel imparted lazily.

'Do you not ride, Terese?' Isabella enquired, and vouchsafed contentedly—'Tio Manuel is the bestest instructor.'

So he may be, Terese thought wryly, but unless I can help it he's not going to instruct me. Summoning a smile, she began gathering the crockery and cutlery together in an attempt to evade giving a direct answer.

'I'll come down and watch you ride for a while, but I must get back within an hour or so to begin preparing dinner,' she said quietly a few minutes later when

Manuel had left the kitchen, presumably to change into more suitable clothes.

'*Si*, Terese,' the little girl said solemnly. 'But I think Tio Manuel means you to ride, too.'

'Tomorrow, perhaps,' Terese compromised brightly, inwardly determined that nothing short of brute force would see her astride a horse, the subject of Manuel's instruction.

In dark denim jeans and a black chunky jumper Manuel presented a formidable, almost piratical figure, and it wasn't difficult to imagine at least one conquistador among his ancestors. The look he swept her when she refused, albeit politely, his help to mount the docile mare he had saddled held a compelling sense of purpose.

'You have no need to be afraid,' he advised placatingly. 'Come, I will lift you up.'

'I'd much prefer to watch Isabella,' she asserted adamantly, turning her attention towards the warmly-clad child happily astride her cantering pony more than a hundred yards away.

'*Gran cielo!* Must you defy me in everything?' His voice was pitched low and held anger as he swung himself into the saddle. His eyes raked her ruthlessly, and Terese involuntarily shivered as he leant down and grasped her about the waist to lift her with remarkable ease to sit in front of him.

'I hate you!' Terese gasped furiously as he reached for the reins with one hand and encircled her waist with the other. 'Just you wait, Manuel Delgado!' Desperately she tried to prise his arm loose and failed miserably to make any impression against his iron-like clasp.

'Your threats arouse in me fear of the good *Dios* himself,' he drawled sardonically, tightening his hold considerably so that she was intensely aware of him with every fibre of her being.

'If I had my way, even the good *Dios* would not absolve you,' she assured bitterly, hating herself for enjoying his strength.

'Why, *querida?*' he laughed softly as he sought the soft skin of her neck with his lips. 'Because I married you for the sole purpose of "making babies", as Isabella so charmingly calls it?'

'At least you're honest enough to admit it!' she flung at him resentfully.

'Ah, but it is good that we are honest with each other, is it not? We do not hide behind the cloak of hypocrisy —no?'

Terese wished she could see his expression. His tone was enigmatic, but she could have sworn he was smiling. She sat in tight-lipped silence as he set the mare moving slowly around the paddock and uttered a startled gasp when it broke into a smart trot.

'You wish to grasp the reins?'

She shook her head, not trusting herself to speak.

'Time enough tomorrow,' Manuel said close to her ear, and a deep chuckle escaped his throat as she angrily tossed her head away.

They drew close to Isabella, and Manuel pulled on the reins a little to match the slower speed of the little girl's pony.

'Isn't it wonderful, Terese? You cannot be afraid with Tio Manuel riding with you.'

Terese managed a suitable monosyllabic reply, then uttered a strangled gasp as her husband softly remarked with dry amusement.

'Perhaps you are more afraid of the man than the beast? Or is it possible you think the man is more beast than man?' He brought the mare to a halt and swung down to the ground with lithe ease, lifting her from the saddle with hard hands at her slim waist. 'I think you have had enough for today.'

Terese was supremely conscious of Isabella's presence, and because of it she thanked him pleasantly before turning to assure the little girl that she intended to watch for a while.

It was something of a relief to escape back to the house and occupy herself with preparing dinner. To be in her husband's constant company for the next thirty-six hours was somewhat daunting, for it was becoming obvious he intended using his undoubted physical magnetism to break down her defences against him. He possessed her body, but not her heart—never that, she determined fiercely as she prepared the sauce for the pasta and set about boning the chicken.

She worked diligently and had everything under control when Manuel strolled into the kitchen with Isabella close at his side almost two hours later.

'Mmn, something smells awfully nice, Terese,' the bright little imp complimented. 'What are we to have?'

'It's to be a surprise, so you shall just have to wait and see,' Terese grinned companionably.

'It would appear the art of cooking is one of your many talents,' Manuel smiled, and ruffled Terese's hair with a careless hand.

'Perhaps you'd better wait and sample your dinner before you pass comment,' she advised deprecatorily as she lifted saucepan lids and stirred the contents with a slight frown, sure of her quickening pulse at his close proximity.

'Come, Isabella,' Manuel chuckled as he caught his niece's hand. 'We will wash, change, and adjourn to the lounge for a game of dominoes, *si?* Most cooks prefer to be alone in the kitchen.'

'Yes, go—both of you,' Terese grimaced laughingly at them. 'In an hour you shall eat.'

There was only the table to set, and she chose the elegance of the dining-room for their evening meal, taking pleasure in setting place-mats on the beautiful rectangle-shaped mahogany table, the use of silver cutlery and fine bone-china plates. It was already dusk, and with sudden inspiration she elected to switch on only the wall-lamps, and discovered two sets of candlesticks and some new candles which she left ready to light. With a quick inspection of the contents on the stove to ensure all could be left alone for the time it would take to get changed she moved into the bedroom, shedding jeans and jumper for an elegant skirt of bottle-green wool-jersey and a matching jumper in fine cashmere. She added a gold pendant on a long gold chain about her neck, brushed her hair and added a touch of colour to her lips. There, that should do. She surveyed her reflection critically in the mirror, then sped hastily back to the kitchen.

The meal was entirely successful—even Terese had to accede to that, and both Manuel and Isabella's enthusiastically-voiced compliments were pleasing, particularly the little girl's praise of the steamed pudding.

It was well after nine when Isabella settled down to sleep, for they had played dominoes and cards after dinner and the bedtime story Manuel told brought forth a host of questions so that the answering proved almost as lengthy as the story.

'You wish to view television?'

Terese cast a somewhat startled backward glance in Manuel's direction as he closed the door of the lounge

111

behind him and moved leisurely towards her. 'I don't mind—whatever you want,' she replied with a slight shrug.

'My, my,' he commented musingly. 'What if I were to take you up on that? Ah,' his dark eyes gleamed wickedly, 'I see the danger signals—you are poised ready to attack. Relax, *querida*. I much prefer tussling with you in the privacy of our bedroom. Besides,' he said dryly, 'it would be pleasant if we could spend a few hours together without resorting to our usual conflicting opinions that inevitably end in argument.'

'In that case, it would be advisable to switch on the television,' Terese evinced sweetly. 'We don't seem to be able to converse for more than five minutes without arguing. I'll make the coffee while you choose which programme we're to watch.'

Manuel executed a slight mocking bow in her direction before consulting with the television magazine, and she couldn't help the feeling he was merely biding his time.

It didn't take long to set out cups and saucers while the percolator brewed fresh coffee, and she placed everything on a tray and carried it through to the lounge, seeing as she entered that he had drawn a small coffee-table close to the double settee, one half of which he comfortably occupied.

Darn him! He knew very well she would opt to sit anywhere else in the room but close at his side. She could tell from the faint quizzical lift of one eyebrow that he was just waiting for her to demur, and a perverse little imp within her head prompted her to do exactly the opposite.

'Your coffee, Manuel,' she offered politely, handing him his cup and saucer. 'If you'll tell me where the *coñac* is kept, I'll fetch it before I sit down.' She silently commended herself for appearing such a dutiful wife as she selected the correct bottle from among a by no means meagre variety in the cabinet opposite.

'You make an excellent cup of coffee.'

Terese turned a cool glance in his direction. 'Thank you,' she voiced solemnly, then returned her attention to the television screen where it appeared *Kojak* had been his choice of the programmes offering.

'Isabella enjoyed her dessert sufficiently to request a second serving.'

'I'm glad,' she replied simply. 'I don't imagine boarding school fare is particularly inspiring.'

Manuel replaced his empty coffee cup down on to the table, then leant well back and stretched one arm out along the back of the settee. 'I imagine nutrition is the main objective,' he murmured thoughtfully, reflecting idly—'*Tortillas*, beans and rice was the staple diet during my sojourn within institutional educational walls.'

'I can't imagine you as a little boy,' Terese considered mildly. 'Particularly an *obedient* little boy,' she elaborated.

'Ah, but I was,' he smiled a little. 'My *padre* played very much the role of—how do you say it?—the heavy father? Self-discipline was something Vicente and I learned at an early age.'

Terese looked at him with interest. 'Didn't you mind being sent to boarding school?'

'Why should I have objected? My father's wealth ensured that I had the best education possible, with tutors for those few subjects in which I was less apt. So it shall be with my sons.'

'Boarding school from the approximate age of twelve

113

is reasonable, but I would never allow my children to attend before then,' she declared adamantly.

Manuel's eyes darkened fractionally, and his voice when he spoke was totally without humour. 'Are you not forgetting that your sons will also be *my* sons?'

Terese glanced quickly away. 'That is something I endeavour not to give too much thought,' she answered bleakly.

'You still believe that upon your stepfather's death you can escape the sanctity of our marriage?'

Bravely she met the dangerous implacability in his gaze and involuntarily lifted her head a little. 'Would it matter so very much?' she asked quietly.

'Yes,' he answered, deliberately examining her features as he traced an idle finger along her cheekbone. 'Be assured I would search until I found you, and never again would you dare to leave me.'

'How you must hate me,' she whispered shakily.

His expression hardened. 'Think what you wish, *mi mujer*—my woman.'

She couldn't just sit there beside him, she had to escape—if only for a few minutes. 'I'll take the tray out to the kitchen.' Was that really her voice so quiet that it was scarcely more than a whisper? She stood to her feet and moved quickly to the door as her vision began to blur, and in the solitude of the kitchen washed and rinsed the contents of the supper tray with life-depending dedication.

'Terese.'

She felt her hands tremble at the sound of that deep dry voice so close behind, and her attempt to move beyond his grasp proved futile.

'Little fool,' Manuel uttered explicitly as he turned her round to face him. 'You think I married you solely as a

114

form of revenge?' One hand moved to lightly cup her chin. 'That I could not have found a suitable wife to bear my heirs from any number of willing women? *Sagrada Madre!*'

She stood there completely numbed, with not one coherent thought capable of coming to mind.

'Ay-ay-ay,' he sighed expressively as he drew her close against him. 'The ways of a Spaniard you find difficult to comprehend—particularly this Spaniard, *si*?'

Terese felt his lips touch her hair, and seconds later the warmth of his fingers slid to her nape and began a soothing movement that brought alive a sensual awareness she found difficult to ignore. To remain like this in silent acquiescence was madness—a madness she couldn't afford.

As if he sensed her inner turmoil he allowed her to move away from his arms, and he stood observing the conflicting emotions chase expressively across her features.

'Come,' he bade quietly. 'Sit with me in the lounge, and so that we do not argue we will not attempt polite conversation.' He smiled slightly. 'A silent truce—but a truce nonetheless, hmmn?'

'Is that possible?' Terese queried shakily.

'Some would say anything is possible if one tries hard enough, *querida*,' he allowed thoughtfully. 'Always it is better to be more optimist than pessimist in order to achieve one's objective.'

She walked with him in contemplative silence and voiced no protest when he drew her down beside him on the settee in the lounge. *Kojak* was barely half-way through and the slick dialogue and action soon held her attention even though it was impossible to ignore Manuel's disturbing presence. The arm that curved around her shoulder was hard and warm, and now and then he raised an idle hand to her hair as if the feel of its silky smoothness afforded him pleasure. It would have been all too easy to relax her guard a little—even to enjoy the feeling of contentment that gradually crept over her.

An hour later Manuel stood indolently to his feet, moving lazily to pour them each a glass of *coñac*, and he shook his head reprovingly when Terese wrinkled her nose in distaste as he handed her a tumbler of the fiery liquid. He resumed his seat beside her and watched idly as she sipped the contents.

A feeling of warm somnolence pervaded every vein in her body and brought a soft smile to her lips as he removed the empty glass from her hand. 'I doubt I could ever become a seasoned drinker when such a small measure of brandy can render me mellow,' she contemplated musingly.

'In the lounge of your home and in the company of your husband—what have you to fear?' Manuel quirked an eyebrow in amusement.

'Ah, but that would be telling,' Terese reiterated whimsically, 'and I won't—tell you, I mean.'

'Perhaps you *should* have some more *coñac*,' he chuckled lightly as he trailed the tips of his fingers along the edge of her lips. 'Then I might be able to persuade you to impart whatever it is you consider I shouldn't be told, hmmn?'

Terese couldn't tear her eyes away from that dark, faintly quizzical face only inches from her own, and of their own volition her fingers traced the firm outline of his mouth and made a tentative exploration of the deep crease running up towards his prominent cheekbone.

116

Her eyes widened into huge liquid-amber pools as he turned his head slightly and pressed warm lips to the inner softness of her palm.

'Why, Manuel?' The oblique query was scarcely more than a whisper.

'It is so important that you know the *why* of it?' he asked gently, and his fingers tangled in her hair as his eyes held hers for what seemed an interminable time, then his lips touched a fleeting caress to each corner of her mouth and travelled across the delicate cheekbone to the lobe of her ear and back again, lightly pressing closed each eyelid in turn. 'Ah, *querida*—if I were to tell you, you would not believe me.'

His kiss began as a gentle exploration and held a dreamy sweetness to which Terese began to respond, and she didn't protest moments later when he lifted her from the settee and purposely strode towards their room.

A further riding lesson was in store for Terese the following morning, and this time she didn't refuse Manuel's help to mount the docile mare perchance he chose to repeat the previous afternoon's example of seating her in the saddle in front of him. She had to own that the sensation of moving slowly astride a horse was a pleasant one, although the thought of galloping at speed at some future time was slightly daunting. As with all things, one improved with practice, she perceived idly as she listened to Manuel's tolerantly voiced instructions.

Sunday turned out to be a lazily spent day, as when both Terese and Isabella's riding lessons were over, Manuel viewed the uncertain skies and declared they would risk an outdoor barbecue lunch. Washed down

117

with beer, the thick juicy steaks between equally thick toasted bread tasted uncommonly good, and afterwards they barely managed to make it indoors before the rain made itself felt in no uncertain terms. Dinner was partaken earlier than usual as Isabella had to be back at the convent by seven o'clock, but they played several games of cards during the afternoon, which proved hilarious in most cases as the stakes were in the form of forfeits thought up by each of them in turn. Isabella's tended to be outrageous, and once had Terese owing Manuel ten kisses which she insisted be given there and then, much to Terese's chagrin and Manuel's amusement. He appeared not a whit embarrassed and even chuckled devilishly when his niece suggested he had better help Terese along a bit as pecks on the cheek were not *real* kisses. It was something of a relief for Terese to escape into the kitchen to prepare dinner!

A strange kind of excitement was building up inside her as the evening passed and became night. Try as she might she couldn't help the wild surge of relief that Manuel was departing on the morrow and she would thus be free from his disturbing presence for at least a few days. She looked forward to spending as much time as she wished with Steve, and she would meet Meg for dinner and they would have an evening out together— perhaps attend a cinema in town, she mused thoughtfully.

CHAPTER SEVEN

'WHAT devious schemes are you plotting, *niña?*'

Terese viewed her husband cautiously across the breakfast table and took a tentative bite from the slice of toast she held before answering—'What makes you think they might be devious?'

A slight smile lifted the corner of his mouth as he sat back in his chair and stirred sugar into his coffee. 'Ah, but I suspect they would not wholly meet with my approval, is this not so?'

A flash of animosity lit her eyes and her chin tilted slightly. 'Do you intend placing me under guard, or even house arrest during your absence?'

His eyes narrowed and his expression became grim. 'Your choice of words is somewhat careless,' he warned bleakly. 'Further remarks in that vein will surely bring my hand into hurtful contact with your well-shaped derriere.'

Terese sat in silence, unsure that she could voice anything calmly in reply to his hateful threat. Truth to tell, she hadn't intended to be so obviously flippant— the words had just slipped from her tongue before she'd given them much thought.

'No doubt it would be too much to expect you to accompany me to the airport?' Manuel queried quizzically some few minutes later. 'No? Then Santanas will drop you off at your stepfather's house when he drives me to Tullamarine.'

'Thank you.'

'Hmmn,' he observed with a touch of humour. 'I'm

not sure such meekness becomes you. Always there will be this fire and ice between us—quiescence is not an integral part of my character, nor yours,' he concluded dryly.

'Perhaps you should have chosen a wife who was meek and mild—at least it would have made for marital bliss,' Terese retorted quickly.

'Perhaps,' he allowed quizzically. 'But a trifle dull, wouldn't you say?'

She finished her coffee and stood to her feet, only to pause as Manuel leant forward and caught her arm in a steely grip.

'I want your word that wherever you go while I am away you will ask Santanas to drive you, and will not venture anywhere alone—especially at night.'

Terese stifled an expressive sigh. 'Oh really, Manuel, I'm not a child!' She cast him a cross look and attempted to free her arm with little success. 'I've driven myself to and from the hospital on numerous occasions late at night and nothing untoward has happened.'

'Nevertheless, Santanas has been instructed to accompany you,' he stated firmly.

'Your trust in me is reassuring,' she said bitterly as she tried once more to wrench her arm out of his grasp.

'My trust in you, *querida*,' he began musingly, 'is not in question—so you can take the light of battle from your furious eyes and apply reason to my request.'

'Request?' she expostulated grimly. 'You don't *request* anything, Manuel. You issue orders, willy-nilly, and *insist* they be obeyed.'

'You would have cause for complaint if I cared little for your welfare,' he reprimanded mildly as he pulled her towards him, laughing at her struggles to escape. 'Come, we will not fight. Instead, you will wish your

120

Spanish *esposo* safe flight and bestow a wifely kiss that will tide him well while he is away, hmmn?'

Somehow she was sitting on his knee, his arms holding her captive, and she raised startled eyes to his.

'Here? Sofia might come in.'

'Being the discreet soul she is, Sofia will quietly go out again,' he smiled gently, and a devilish gleam appeared in those dark eyes so close to her own. 'I would suggest the bedroom, but that could lead to my missing the plane. However, there are other flights . . .' He began to chuckle at her outraged expression and slid a hand beneath the heavy curtain of her hair, drawing her head back against his shoulder as he fixed his mouth on hers with a gentleness that turned her bones to water. There was a wealth of seduction in the manner his lips explored hers and when he gently extricated her arms from about his neck there was a certain amount of regret in his voice. 'If I do not make the effort *now*, I will indeed miss this morning's flight,' he said wryly as he placed her on her feet and moved with easy fluidity to stand beside her. 'Go tidy your hair and get your coat. I have to retrieve my briefcase from the study, and undoubtedly Santanas is patiently awaiting us.'

Terese quickly escaped upstairs and there ran a comb hurriedly through her long disordered tresses, trying valiantly to ignore the mirrored reflection of her bright eyes and flushed cheeks.

Manuel was waiting by the massive front door as she ran down the stairs, and she couldn't help the feeling of longing that rose momentarily in her breast at the sight of him standing so tall and indomitable. For one mad crazy moment she almost wished he wasn't going away, for the thought of occupying that great bed on her own filled her with an aching loneliness.

She sat beside him in the rear of the Daimler, and when Santanas brought the car to a halt outside Steve's house she somehow expected he would kiss her again, but it appeared not as he let his fingers trail briefly across her cheek to rest against her lips for a few short seconds.

'*Hasta luego, amada,*' Manuel said gently.

Terese scrambled hurriedly from the car as a quietly murmured 'goodbye' left her lips, and it wasn't until the car was out of sight that she remembered the words she had wanted to say. '*Vaya con Dios,*' she whispered softly, then quickly turned and opened the gate.

Mrs Scott was with Steve, and after a quick glance at his pale jaundiced features Terese gave him an affectionate hug that lingered for more than a few seconds as she gathered her composure against the sadness his illness aroused. Remorse filled her as she reflected her own relatively carefree weekend in comparison with his obviously pain-filled one.

'Yes,' she said quietly to Mrs Scott a short while later as they both went into the kitchen to make fresh coffee, 'the doctor must be called this morning. I'll ring him now.'

Mrs Scott spared her a sympathetic glance as she washed Steve's breakfast dishes—a pitiful cup, saucer and spoon. 'I stayed with him until the early hours of this morning, then slipped home for a short sleep. It's very difficult for you, dear, but I really don't think he should be left alone.'

Terese was on the verge of tears as she gratefully thanked the kindly woman. 'I know. My husband is away for a few days, so I'll be able to stay.' No matter what Manuel had exacted by way of a promise from her, she intended facing his anger when he returned, for there was no way she would leave Steve on his own now.

The doctor called just before lunch, a short dapper little man in his fifties, and his prognosis was hardly a happy one. Steve's admittance into hospital was imminent, and he was agreeable in allowing him to remain at home only if Terese could be with him. He left a prescription and promised to call the following morning.

Terese was insistent that Mrs Scott should go home for at least the remainder of the day to catch up on some rest, and this she agreed to do just as soon as Terese arrived back from the chemist with Steve's tablets. It had turned out to be a filthy day with the rain pouring down, and as Terese had no mode of transport she got thoroughly soaked.

Even a hurried shower did little to warm her chilled bones, and Mrs Scott's shocked maternal clucking over her wet state was endearing. She sneezed for much of the afternoon, and by early evening knew herself to be running a temperature which four-hourly doses of paracetamol did little to lesson.

A telephone call to Sofia and a lengthy explanation amid several sneezes disclaimed Terese's need to have Santanas call later in the afternoon to take her back to Toorak, and Sofia's—'But, *señora*, the Señor left definite instructions——' had little effect on her resolve to remain with him.

She finally crept into bed quite late as Steve had found it difficult to settle comfortably, and she slept only lightly, waking frequently to look in on him. It was so cold—she hadn't realised how cold, and in spite of keeping the fire burning low behind a guard in the lounge she seemed to be constantly shivering.

The following morning Mrs Scott was alarmed at her

123

high temperature and hacking cough, and when Doctor Spedding called to check Steve she suggested he prescribe something for Terese.

'My dear young lady, you should be in bed,' he admonished severely. 'You certainly are not capable of looking after your stepfather. A word with you, Mrs Scott, if you please.'

Dutifully Mrs Scott followed him out into the kitchen and they held a hurried conversation—the only results Terese could deduce being several reassuring nods from Mrs Scott.

'Please go to bed. My dear, you won't do Steve any good at all by allowing him to see how ill you are.'

Terese opened her mouth to speak and the words were lost in a spasm of coughing. When she regained her breath her eyes were streaming and she felt weak and decidedly woolly-headed.

'Doctor Spedding will drop a prescription into the chemist for you and it will be delivered later this afternoon,' Mrs Scott advised kindly. 'I'll stay overnight, for in all consciousness I couldn't leave you both to look after each other—it would be a case of the blind leading the blind,' she concluded with an attempt at humour.

Terese expressed her gratitude and slowly undressed for bed, miraculously warmed with hotwater bottles undoubtedly put there by Mrs Scott. She couldn't face food of any description, not even the beef broth offered early in the evening by a worried Mrs Scott, and sips of water with the antibiotic capsules were all she could manage to persuade Terese to take.

By morning Terese seemed worse, and she was unaware of little that took place throughout the day. It was all a hazy blur of voices in between long bouts of racking coughing fits and merciful slumber. She was vaguely aware of Doctor Spedding examining her, then strangely much later—although how much later she couldn't remember—she thought she heard Manuel's voice. That must have been in one of her dreams—she seemed to slip into numerous dreams—for he was in Adelaide and thankfully ignorant. Heavens, she thought weakly, she'd have to be fit before his return or there would be the very devil to pay!

Manuel's image seemed to continually plague her dreams. His was the face that loomed over her while hands gently sponged her fevered skin and changed moisture-soaked pyjamas for dry ones, whose hands continually fixed the bedcovers when she pushed them from her in attempts to cool her heated body.

Then slowly the mist seemed to clear and no longer did she feel so insufferably hot, and mercifully she slept long and dreamlessly to wake in a bed not her own in a room she was unfamiliar with.

Terese let her eyes wander slowly about the dimly-lit room, then turned her head towards the source of light — a bedside lamp glowing atop a small pedestal beside her bed. Beyond the lamp in the shadows a figure moved to unfold its length from a chair.

'So—at last you wake.'

Terese gazed wide-eyed at the unmistakable sound of her husband's voice, and her own voice was scarcely more than a subdued squeak. 'Where am I?'

Manuel came to sit on the edge of her bed. 'Not in hospital, *niña*, although you came very close to it, believe me. You are at home, in a room not far from our own.'

'I don't remember——' she began, only to be interrupted as he effectively silenced her with a finger across her lips.

'It is better that you do not try to talk,' he admonished gently. 'First, you will drink some of Sofia's chicken broth, then I will tell you much of what has happened.'

She watched in idle fascination as he poured some warm broth from a thermos flask into a cup, then lifted her effortlessly to sit back against the pillows. Her eyes never left his dark unfathomable ones for an instant as she sipped the contents of the cup he held to her lips, and even in this light she couldn't help but notice how strained and tired he looked.

'You have been ill since Tuesday,' he began as he placed the empty cup down on to the pedestal. 'Doctor Spedding contacted Santanas on Wednesday morning and a message was immediately relayed to me in Adelaide. I took the next available flight to Melbourne and Santanas met me at the airport, then together we brought you home. You lingered only a hair's breadth from pneumonia for almost two days.' His voice held anger. 'The crisis passed nearly thirty-six hours ago, and since then you have slept,' he paused fractionally, then continued as if he were able to read her thoughts. 'It is now almost eleven o'clock on Sunday evening.'

'You were angry,' Terese whispered despondently.

'Furious,' he agreed, although there was a slight contradictory smile lifting the edges of his mouth. 'During the brief flight from Adelaide I was undoubtedly the most uncivil passenger on board—not even the stewardess dared speak to me, I think. I'm quite sure your capable Mrs Scott imagines you have married a man who is both dragon and devil,' he mused thoughtfully on reflection. 'It is perhaps as well only Santanas was aware just how harshly I swore when we entered your step-

126

father's house and were confronted first with his state of health, then yours.'

'It wasn't a dream that you were with me,' she managed shakily, and her nervous fingers plucked at the edge of the sheet.

'No,' Manuel affirmed quietly.

Her eyes darkened with concern. 'Steve—how is he?' she questioned anxiously.

'His condition has deteriorated, *niña*,' he answered slowly. 'He is in hospital—it was no longer possible for him to remain at home.'

Terese raised anguished eyes to his, and the voiced query died on her lips. Even she knew it would be at least a week before she would be able to visit Steve in hospital, and the expression in Manuel's eyes foretold that any such thoughts to the contrary were impossible.

'No, *niña*,' he said gently. 'Santanas has visited him and he will continue to do so. I will arrange that you speak with Steve by telephone, and the moment the good doctor sanctions it I will myself take you to the hospital. Rest assured that everything possible is being done for him.'

Terese felt one tear spill and slide ignominiously down her cheek, and at his muffled exclamation she said with utter wretchedness—'I'm going to cry,' and like the turning on of a tap the tears coursed silently down her cheeks unchecked.

Manuel's soft curses were unintelligible as he gathered her into his arms, blankets and all, and cradled her against him as if she were a child. When at last the tears ceased he placed her back into the bed and tucked the blankets into position, smiling a little as she caught hold of his hand.

'Si, niña,' he affirmed quietly, 'I will be here—in a bed not five feet away. You have only to call should you need me.'

With sudden perception she knew that he had been with her ever since he had brought her home, and the knowledge brought a strange weakness to her limbs. Without thinking she lifted his hand to her lips and silently whispered her thanks.

'Ay-ay-ay,' he uttered somewhat wryly. 'When I can be little other than one of Isabella's teddy-bears in your arms, you become a seducing minx.'

Terese smiled sleepily and he had to bend low to catch her words—'Such a nice teddy-bear, Manuel.'

Terese improved rapidly, and with the doctor's approval she was permitted to get out of bed for a short while on Wednesday. It was quite an occasion as both Sofia and Maria fussed constantly at her side and were volubly horrified that she should think of attempting to go downstairs. When Manuel returned at the end of the day it was to find her happily ensconced in the *sala*, wrapped almost from neck to toes in an enveloping blanket—against the possible chilled air. Although how even the slightest puff of chilled air could reach her in the centre of a centrally-heated house with the addition of a log fire burning cheerfully in the same room was beyond her! She felt fine, her appetite had almost returned, and she no longer needed to be cosseted, she told Manuel scarcely before he could draw breath upon entering the room.

'You will take things quietly, nevertheless,' he smiled the admonishment as he came to her side.

'You're all of you nothing better than clucking broody hens with only one chick,' Terese declared amiably.

'A little of the fire is returning to your disposition,'

he acknowledged with a dark amusing gleam. 'Before long you will be fighting your Spanish *esposo* with all of your former fervour—*si?*'

'Just to prove I'm almost myself again I shall have dinner downstairs this evening. Tomorrow, I will get dressed.'

'Perhaps,' Manuel allowed quizzically.

Terese wrinkled her nose at him. 'Is the "perhaps" to apply to dinner or getting dressed?'

'Getting dressed,' he replied musingly. 'I can see I'll have nothing less than a riot on my hands if I refuse you dinner.'

'If ever you take ill, Manuel, I shall wield a severe disciplinary stick,' she warned impudently.

'Then I shall have to pray that I do not become ill.' He poured a glass of wine and held it to her lips, permitting just a small amount to escape before partaking a generous quantity himself.

There was a strange intimacy in the gesture, one that stirred her senses and left her feeling oddly restless. 'I spoke to Mrs Scott today,' she said with an odd little rush. 'She is relieved that I am almost recovered—although she very cautiously declined to mention anything about the manner in which you descended a week ago.'

'Did she not?' Manuel chuckled slightly.

'Santanas went to see Steve today,' Terese sobered quickly, and for a moment her expression was treacherously forlorn. 'Neither you nor he will really tell me how Steve is, and what telephone conversations I have been able to have with him have been pitifully brief.'

'I cannot be reassuring, *querida*. You must know that.'

Terese bowed her head. 'No, I suppose not.'

'Come, after dinner I will permit you to beat me at cards, and you may name your stakes,' he cajoled after a long silence, and it was perhaps as well that at that moment Sofia chose to bring in a portable table which she immediately set with a snowy cloth.

The meal had been served to tempt Terese's palate, and it was to Sofia's credit that Terese did full justice to the food, for in all honesty she had little real appetite that evening.

'Well, *querida*, what is it to be?'

Terese looked across at Manuel as he shuffled the cards and unconsciously her eyes pleaded with him. 'Couldn't I go with Santanas tomorrow? I'll wear two jumpers beneath my coat, tights beneath my slacks, gloves and a hat. Santanas can drive me right up to the door.'

He sighed gently. 'Terese, you know I will not agree.'

'Oh, please, Manuel,' she begged tremulously. 'What's the worst that can happen to me? I'm taking antibiotics and my temperature has been consistently normal for the past two days. If you insist on my waiting too long, Steve could die before I see him again.' Her voice was achingly pathetic.

'The worst that can happen is a relapse and probable pneumonia,' he answered bluntly. 'If it were the height of summer I might consider it, but in winter with the temperature outside verging on zero? No, *querida*, most definitely not.'

Terese glimpsed grim implacability in his features and knew he wouldn't relent, and suddenly she felt weary as she stood to her feet. 'I think I'll go to bed.'

'A wise decision.' With ease he swung her into his arms and carried her from the *sala* up the stairs to the bedroom she had occupied for the past week.

'There is nothing you need for the next hour or so?' he queried tolerantly, and she shook her head.

'I don't think there's any necessity now for you to stay with me at night. I—I'd prefer it if you didn't,' she said slowly.

'*Buenas noches*, Terese.' There was a mocking slant to his words and she didn't look up until he had left the room.

Her bed was warm from the electric blanket and she sat up against the pillows determinedly trying to read, but she lacked concentration and every few minutes her attention tended to wander. It was barely nine o'clock and she longed to do something constructive—even viewing television was preferable to sitting up here alone. Darn it, she would put on her long velvet house-coat and go downstairs again. Suiting thought to action, she did just that, padding down the stairs with care to the *sala*.

Eventually she must have dozed, for when she woke it seemed quite late and she felt thirsty and in need of a hot drink. The kitchen was empty—Sofia and Maria had no doubt retired some time ago, and Terese set water to boil and spooned Milo and sugar into a beaker, then decided to make coffee for Manuel as well. Very probably he would still be in the study, and she felt strangely contrite at having said she didn't need him to watch over her. No matter how she tried she couldn't forget the tired strained look on his face when first she'd woken and found him keeping vigil—even Sofia had remarked that the Señor had rarely moved from her side during those five days she had lain so ill.

As she carried the tray across the lobby she began to wonder if indeed he was working, as it was past eleven o'clock and she stifled a smile as she thought how ironic it would be if he had already retired to bed and her good intentions would go unnoticed. Carefully she set the tray on the floor outside the study door, not completely trusting the steadiness of her hand in attempting to open the door and hold the tray with the other. Turning the handle, she pushed the door open and bent down to retrieve the tray, contriving to still the erratic beating of her heart at the sight of Manuel seated behind the desk.

'*Madre de Dios!*' He stood to his feet in one fluid angry movement. 'What in the name of heaven do you think you are doing?'

Terese stood momentarily transfixed at the harshness of his tone and the light of battle entered her veins. Calmly she carried the tray across the room and placed it on his desk.

'Do you have any idea what time of night it is?' he queried with grim softness that in no way belied his anger.

'Yes,' she answered swiftly. 'It's ten minutes past eleven.' Competently she poured out his coffee and added two lumps of sugar before placing it in front of him together with a flask of *coñac*.

'Perhaps you will kindly explain why you are not in bed?'

Terese looked across at him, feeling thoroughly vexed, and stamped her foot. 'Really, Manuel!' she flashed wrathfully. 'I'm tired of being treated like a piece of Dresden china by you, and Sofia—even Santanas is so courteous it's almost funny! All right, I know I've been ill, but I'm scarcely a helpless invalid!' She felt the prick of tears burn the back of her eyelids and at that moment hated him afresh. 'If you must have reasons and explanations—I couldn't stay upstairs, so I came down to the *sala* and watched television, then I must have slept, for when I woke it was quite late and I felt thirsty. I made myself some Milo, and if you must know, I felt terrible at being nasty to you . . .' she trailed off miserably and quickly turned so that he couldn't see her face.

'Precisely how were you nasty?' he queried as he viewed her averted features with interest.

'You know very well what I mean,' she retorted bleakly.

'Ah, yes,' he began lazily, deliberately taking his time. 'You very politely informed me that my nightly role as nursemaid could be considered at an end.' He paused thoughtfully and barely managed to keep the amusement from his voice. 'Perhaps I am to regard the coffee as a peace-offering?' he suggested. '*Si, querida?*'

'No!' Terese threw at him vehemently, thoroughly incensed that he should be amused.

'Little liar,' he said calmly as he moved towards her from behind the desk.

With as much speed as she could muster she sought to escape and managed a few steps before hands caught hold of her shoulders and successfully halted her flight.

'Indeed, you are almost yourself again,' he chuckled as he drew her possessively back against him. Gently his lips sought the sweetly-scented skin at her nape. 'Come, sit down and drink your Milo while I have the coffee.'

Rather shakily she escaped and watched in idle fascination as he leaned nonchalantly against the edge of the desk. There seemed to be a latent sensuality in each and every one of his movements, and she began to wonder if she hadn't overdone things. Her legs seemed decidedly jelly-like and her head felt so light it hardly belonged to her at all.

'Leave it there,' Manuel bade quietly several minutes

133

later as she began to place the cups back on to the tray. 'Sofia will collect it in the morning.'

Terese regarded him with wide luminous eyes and offered no resistance when he swung her up into his arms. She hadn't the strength to fight him even if she wanted to, and much as she hated to admit it there was a deep ache within her and she longed for him with a primitive awareness that astounded as it confounded. The knowledge sent wild colour flooding to her cheeks so that she buried her face against him, thankful that he was occupied in closing the lights.

'*Gracias*, Manuel,' she whispered as he placed her on her feet close to her bed. 'I haven't thanked you for—for looking after me.' She allowed the words to tumble out with a certain desperation.

Gently he took her chin and lifted it, examining her face with intentness that missed little. 'Then thank me.'

For a moment she hesitated, then reaching up she pulled his head down and placed a soft fleeting kiss at one corner of that sensually-moulded mouth.

'Ah, *querida*,' he murmured seriously, 'that is almost an invitation.'

Hardly aware of doing so, she repeated the action and felt his lips move over hers as he drew her close against him, and his touch evoked a response she didn't attempt to hide.

During the following days Terese showed remarkable progress and the weekend brought Isabella home so anxiously solicitous over Terese's welfare that Terese was obliged to reassure the little girl that she really hadn't come *that* close to dying! It took most of Saturday to convince her that all Terese had suffered from

134

was a severe chill that unfortunately had developed into pleurisy.

There was a pleasant surprise awaiting Terese on Monday morning in that Manuel gave his permission for her to visit Steve at the hospital—that was the pleasant part—and the surprise was his voiced intention to accompany her himself.

She looked askance at his decision as he sat across the table from her over breakfast.

'Manuel? Surely it isn't necessary?' she queried incredulously. 'Santanas will take me.'

He cast her a curiously penetrating glance as he drained the remaining contents of his coffee cup. 'Suffice it that I consider it necessary, *querida*,' he replied firmly.

And that, Terese perceived somewhat wryly, was that!

'I will arrive home in time for lunch, after which we will leave, *si*? You will inform Sofia?'

'Yes, of course,' she answered carefully, viewing him circumspectly from beneath her lashes as he stood to his feet and took his leave. Well! Why would he decide to come with her? No matter how much she thought about it she still couldn't think of a logical reason.

On the way to the hospital she became lost in retrospective thought, desperately hoping that Steve had not slipped too close to the edge of life's precipice. All her nursing instincts warned her that she must be prepared to see a change in him, and probably a drastic change. Manuel walked at her side in silence, and she was grateful that he offered no banal pleasantries in an attempt to distract the reserve of courage she needed to draw upon in order to be brave in Steve's presence. Somehow she would need to smile and laugh a little, and let him know she cared, and above all she mustn't let him sense the hidden tears she knew would be just beneath the surface. She had seen young children die, literally, and she had been sad—she had even wept. But this was something else. A young mother's tear-wet voice came to mind and Terese blinked as the words whispered in her mind—'It's different when they're your own'—and it was true, for it was.

Afterwards, Terese never quite knew how she came to be sitting in the car with Manuel, for the time between when she left Steve's side until Manuel slid into the car beside her was not retained in her memory.

'He hasn't long.' Her voice sounded strange, almost as if it belonged to someone else.

'No,' Manuel agreed quietly.

'You knew, didn't you?'

'On your behalf I have kept in daily contact with the hospital staff, yes,' he answered sombrely.

'I think I'm going to cry,' she offered shakily some minutes later.

'Then cry, *niña*,' he said gently. 'Such tears are nothing of which to be ashamed.'

It wasn't easy to erase Steve's image from her mind, and even in sleep she couldn't rest easily. In the morning her pillow was damp with the silent tears she had shed, and her loss of appetite had Sofia shaking her head with unvoiced disapproval.

There was little anyone could say or do to help the pain inside her heart, and during dinner that evening when Santanas entered apologetically to speak quietly with Manuel, she sensed then that it was all over. Santanas remained in the dining-room while Manuel took the call in his study, and Terese knew her instinct was correct. One look at his face was sufficient, from the sympathetic kindness so evident, and when Manuel returned a few minutes later it was there in his eyes.

Time is a great healer—how many times had she heard that said—indeed, how many times she had offered those very words herself in an attempt at condolence?

Much of the week that followed was a merciful blur. The funeral had been the worst moment, for then the tears came—they seemed to come for a long time. Then, gradually, common sense began to prevail. Steve would have wished her to remember him in health, not in mourning, and at the weekend Manuel drove down to the stud farm at Dandenong where the horses and Isabella's subdued chatter provided a welcome diversion. A long walk in relative hillside country seemed to bring a certain peace of mind, and although spring was still a few months distant there was evidence that nature was preparing for the re-birth of yet another cycle.

Somewhere the thought entered Terese's mind that now she was free—the invisible tie that had held her to Manuel was dissolved by Steve's death, and if she wished to brave her husband's wrath she could carefully plan to disappear from his life. A laugh left her lips. Free? Free? It seemed ironical that during those first few weeks of her marriage all that had kept her sane was the moment when Steve's death would provide her release from marital bondage. And now? Her Spanish *esposo* held her captive as successfully as if she wore chains linking her to his side. If being free meant leaving him, she had no wish to savour such freedom.

CHAPTER EIGHT

Exactly eight days after Steve's funeral, Doña Luisa Pereira Delgado arrived in Melbourne from Brisbane together with Emilia Gomez. Manuel had driven the Daimler to meet them at the airport while Terese waited nervously at home. Nervously, because the prospect of meeting Manuel's mother filled her with apprehension, and she entertained the niggling doubt that Doña Luisa was as yet unacquainted with her son's recent marriage. In fact it wouldn't surprise her in the least if he decided to present his mother with a fait accompli!

Terese's first impression of Doña Luisa was that of an elegant *lady* in every sense of the word whose regal bearing was almost stately. It didn't take long to ascertain that although Doña Luisa was somewhat of a paragon of class and good breeding there was a total lack of arrogance in her manner. Of medium height, she was comfortably proportioned with a deep olive complexion, dark hair swept back into an elegant chignon, and her dark liquid eyes twinkled whenever she smiled. Outwardly composed, she had greeted her daughter-in-law with just the right measure of friendliness and affection as was fitting to the occasion.

About Emilia Gomez Terese held slight reservations, for although she seemed painstakingly quiet and demure almost to the point of timidity it was difficult to tell whether it was natural or a pose.

However, after partaking of sherry in the *sala* and having dined in the formal dining-room Terese began to suspect that the Spanish girl found Manuel's dynamic masculinity somewhat awe-inspiring. She couldn't help the slight musing smile as a fleeting intuitive thought flashed through her mind that Emilia would probably regard physical sex as a duty to be borne rather than a mutual exploratory pleasure, and possibly would be relieved, not scandalised, if her husband took a mistress.

'And my dear little *nieta*—my Isabella —how is she?'

Terese couldn't help the warm smile that sprang to her lips as Doña Luisa mentioned Isabella, and as the query had been directed equally to both Manuel and herself, she voiced an enthusing—'Fine'—and glanced towards her husband.

'You shall see for yourself tomorrow,' Manuel responded tolerantly. 'I have no arrangements for the weekend in mind, although a few dinner invitations have been extended—over which we will confer during the weekend.'

Doña Luisa inclined her head graciously. 'There are a few old friends, of course, but for much of my visit I wish to become better acquainted with Terese. While you busily engaged at work, Manuel, I will take both Terese and Emilia shopping,' she declared, and sent her son a startling smile. 'You shall meet us for lunch—we will arrange a day.'

'But of course—it will be a pleasure,' he assented warmly. 'Santanas will be placed entirely at your disposal.'

'*Gracias.*' Doña Luisa turned towards Terese and smiled slowly. 'One can see why Manuel made haste to make you his bride. Your hair is utterly beautiful.'

Manuel reached out an idle hand and lifted a stray tendril between his fingers. '*Exquisita,* is it not, Madre?' he agreed amiably. 'It is, however, only one of many attributes—one does not marry solely for the beauty of

139

the hair.' His dark eyes gleamed with laughter and quite deliberately he leant down and bestowed a lingering kiss against his wife's temple.

'Of course not, *mihijo*,' Doña Luisa twinkled unrepentantly.

Terese looked from one to the other of them and tried to hide her confusion, her eyes for one instant flaring angrily alive as they met the gentle mockery in the dark eyes not far from her own.

'Ah, *amada*,' Manuel chided softly.

'He likes to tantalise, this son of mine,' Doña Luisa began placatingly. 'You must give him back as good as he gives you, my dear. What is it now?' she mused thoughtfully. 'Ah, yes—what is sauce for the gander is also sauce for the goose—that is correct, *si*?'

Manuel chuckled deeply as he raised his hands heavenward. '*Madre mia!* Do not encourage her to answer me back—already she has proved to possess something of a temper!'

'I am pleased that she has,' his mother replied calmly.

'Quarrelling is so—boorish,' Emilia offered with a slight grimace of distaste. 'It is more refined for a wife to be amenable with her husband's wishes.'

Oh, mercy! Terese breathed silently. 'Don't you agree that a wife is entitled to her own opinions, Emilia—even if they differ from those of her husband?' she queried solemnly, and didn't dare glance towards Manuel.

'If a wife has a differing opinion, she should not voice it,' Emilia proclaimed earnestly. 'A husband prefers docility and a smoothly-run household.'

My, my! sighed Terese meditatively. Stay in this house for very long and your eyebrows will become permanently raised! 'Obviously our ideas are different because of our nationalities,' she remarked kindly. 'I was taught free expression both at school and at home in the belief it was better to discuss problems rather than to seethe in silence.'

'Doesn't that tend to make your argumentative?'

'Very,' Manuel declared with a wry smile. 'But never dull.'

'I do not consider amenability to be dull,' Emilia protested with a slight frown.

'No,' Manuel agreed gently. 'However, you had a very strict convent education, and in Spain much goes by tradition, does it not?'

'Do you not consider tradition important?'

Oh, Emilia, you'll never win an argument with Manuel! Terese spared her a glance and began to wonder if much of Emilia's ideas were not relegated theory—perhaps there was hope for the girl, after all!

'Providing it does not lose touch with today's reality —si.'

'The complexities of such an argument cannot be resolved in merely one evening,' Doña Luisa declared smoothly. 'I find travelling rather tiring at my age, so if you will forgive my absence I will retire to my room.' Without further ado she rose to her feet, bade them each a fond goodnight and made her way upstairs.

Emilia glanced from Manuel to Terese and stood rather awkwardly. 'I will retire also—if you will excuse me.'

'There is no need to, if you are not tired,' Terese began gently. 'Neither Manuel nor I go to bed early.'

'Not every evening,' Manuel declared with a decidedly devilish twinkle, laying light but deliberate stress to his words.

Emilia coloured painfully and muttered a hurried, 'Buenas noches,' then almost fled from the room.

'You've succeeded in shocking her,' Terese accused in a subdued whisper just as soon as the door closed.

'Perhaps I have,' he drawled musingly.

'There's no *perhaps* about it,' she said indignantly. 'And what's more, you did it deliberately.'

'*Querida*, your feathers are ruffled.' His dark eyes gleamed a trifle wickedly as he drew her to her feet and bent his head down to hers. 'Madre is charming, is she not? You will enjoy each other's company, I think—*si*?'

Terese moved her head away and endeavoured to escape as his arms drew her closely against him. 'Yes,' she managed in a muffled voice.

'You are cross, are you not, because I sought to tease a little?' Manuel chuckled as he lifted her with ease and settled his lengthy frame into a nearby armchair. 'Sit still, *niña*. If you continue to wriggle about on my lap like that, I will have little option but to hoist you over one shoulder and stride purposely upstairs to bed— where I shall commit what no doubt the good Emilia would consider unmentionable and scandalous deeds.'

His wry humour was apt, and Terese lifted laughing eyes to his. 'You're a terrible man, Manuel Delgado.'

'Ah, *si*,' he agreed mockingly. 'Undoubtedly Emilia offers thankful prayers to the good *Dios* each night and morning that she has escaped my tyranny.'

'She will make an extremely dutiful wife,' Terese commented idly. 'Doña Luisa thought so, and brought her here as a suitable prospective bride—for you.'

'Knowing full well that any bride I took would be of my own choosing, and Emilia least of all.'

'You resemble that nursery rhyme about the little girl—"when she was good she was very, very good, and when she was bad she was horrid",' she recited a trifle impudently.

Manuel trailed an idle hand across her throat and beneath the heavy swathe of vibrant hair at her nape his fingers began a subtle massage that sent shivers up and down her spine.

'I well remember those angry words you hurled at me on the first occasion you entered my home.'

She swallowed involuntarily at the hint of anger in his voice and chose to comment guardedly, 'You were insufferably arrogant that evening.'

'You set to put me in my place, did you not—and be damned to the consequences?'

'Knowing Steve, and the circumstances—I was furious,' she agreed pensively.

'That you were,' he stated wryly. 'A veritable firebrand.'

His kiss was far from gentle and drew a hurt murmur of protest and a look of reproach from her eyes as she struggled to free herself. There were tears prickling her eyelids, and try as she might there was no escape from the hard pressure of his fingers as they gripped her chin and forced her to meet his gaze. For several seconds she thought he meant to exact further punishment and of its own volition her lower lip began to tremble. It took considerable effort to control her tears and she was intensely aware of how vulnerable she was at his hands.

'Ay-ay-ay,' he breathed regretfully. 'That was unfair, was it not? The memory of that evening—and others—fills me with anger and the desire to punish is uppermost. *Por Dios,*' he swore softly as one solitary tear spilled and ran slowly down her cheek. 'Do not cry, *querida*—I beg of you.' Those last few words came out as a remorseful groan and were immediately followed by a somewhat savage volume of Spanish which to Terese was incomprehensible. Even as he spoke he stood to his feet with her

143

in his arms and moved to the door to switch off the lights, then mounted the stairs with ease.

Saturday dawned bright and clear with barely a cloud in sight, the air bitingly sharp and feet-stamping cold. It seemed as if the wet windy squalls of winter had vanished and Terese couldn't help wondering if it were not an omen of some kind.

Together with Doña Luisa and Emilia, Manuel and Terese left early after breakfast to collect an excited Isabella from the convent, and the little girl's flow of words kept them entertained until well after lunch.

The rapport between Isabella and Doña Luisa was delightful, and Terese's intention to remain quietly in the background became impossible as Isabella constantly drew her into their conversation. Manuel came in for similar treatment and tended to view his niece with amused indulgence. Only Emilia sat slightly out of the family circle and contributed little by way of conversation, although to be perfectly fair to the girl she had scant opportunity to voice anything as Isabella seemed intent on informing her grandmother of every solitary detail that had taken place since they had last met—some five weeks previously!

As a special concession the evening meal was brought forward an hour so that Isabella could join them, and Manuel announced during dinner that his niece might be permitted to eat with the adults for the duration of her school vacation.

'Oh, Tio Manuel!' Isabella's eyes glowed with pleasure. 'You are the bestest *tio* in all the world—a whole two weeks!'

'Not every night, *chica*,' he warned smilingly. 'There will be a few evenings when we dine out, and then you must have an early supper and go to bed. Too many late nights and you will not have the energy to accompany Abuelita, Terese and Emilia on those shopping expeditions—*si?*'

'*Si*, Tio Manuel,' the little girl willingly agreed. 'Terese said we might go to the cinema together.' She paused, searching for the right phrase with care. 'If it meets with your approval,' she added with immense satisfaction. 'And please can we visit Luna Park?'

Manuel began to chuckle and his eyes gleamed darkly as he regarded first Isabella and then Terese. 'I begin to think this vacation is a planned conspiracy with an outing arranged for almost every day. Very well, but on the condition that I myself accompany you both to Luna Park. I think, somehow, that your *abuela* would not enjoy an afternoon's entertainment at the Park,' he concluded lightly.

'Such an occasion will provide me with an excellent excuse to rest,' Doña Luisa twinkled gaily, 'while Emilia gladly becomes involved with a book, I imagine.'

'Gladly,' Emilia interposed quickly, before Manuel or Terese could courteously extend her an invitation to join them. The thought of visiting an amusement park was slightly beneath her dignity and showed rather plainly on her face.

'I have one request,' Doña Luisa began kindly, 'and that is to witness Isabella ride the pony she has told me so much about.'

'Tomorrow,' Manuel agreed. 'Much as I would like to place myself entirely at your disposal for the following fortnight, it is unfortunately impossible. A few pressing business appointments cannot be put aside in light of my being absent in Sydney almost immediately after you and Emilia leave for Europe, Madre.'

'Manuel, your company is expected only whenever you can be free to give it,' his mother assured him mildly.

'*Gracias*,' he acknowledged tolerantly.

Sunday was devoted entirely to Isabella, and after a leisurely breakfast Manuel set an unusually sedate pace behind the wheel of the Daimler to the stud farm at Dandenong.

Terese was grateful to be spared giving an account of her riding ability, although for a moment she thought Manuel intended her to have a further lesson. Emilia had brought her riding gear along and seemed to enjoy a brisk canter around the paddock. On learning there was to be a show-jumping competition at the Pony Club that afternoon she became elated, and her enthusiasm coupled with Isabella's excitement brought a promise from Manuel that they could all attend after lunch.

When they arrived there was a gala in progress to raise funds for the Pony Club and various stalls were placed strategically to gather patronage from the spectators present. After the first round of events Terese suggested that Isabella might like to investigate the stalls, and it was as they were wandering among these that she bumped into none other than Nadine Norcroft.

'Well, well, if it isn't the very new Señora Delgado,' Nadine greeted cynically, and one eyebrow arched itself suggestively. 'Complete with acquired family, I see. Taking your duties seriously, aren't you, sweetie?'

'I don't regard Isabella as a duty,' Terese replied evenly, and she clasped Isabella's hand more tightly within her own as she gave Nadine a particularly direct look that the other chose to ignore.

'No, you wouldn't. At a guess I think you might even like the little beasts.' Nadine smiled with artificial

146

brightness down towards Isabella. 'I'm a friend of your Uncle Manuel.'

Isabella surveyed her with unblinking deliberation, then offered doubtfully, 'Are you?'

'A very close friend,' Nadine confirmed with calculated significance.

'I think we should be getting back,' Terese suggested firmly as she tried not to show her dislike of the other woman.

'Yes, run away, do,' Nadine evinced sweetly. 'I find children particularly tiresome.'

'Terese isn't a child,' Isabella corrected defensively as she gazed dubiously up at Nadine.

'My, my, aren't you the clever one!' Nadine said sarcastically to Terese, and swept her a spiteful glance. 'On your side and ready to spring to your defence. You must possess *something*, after all.'

'Oh, but I do,' Terese returned disparagingly as she felt the anger within her rise to boiling point. 'I succeeded where you failed—remember?'

'Don't count your chickens, darling.'

'I wouldn't dream of doing so, Nadine. Come, Isabella,' Terese bade gently. 'I'm sure Miss Norcroft wants to get back to watch the jumping. Would you like a toffee-apple?'

'*Si*, Terese.'

'Don't get all sticky, children, will you?' With this parting shot Nadine left them, and Terese uttered a vexed sigh of relief.

'I don't think that lady really is a friend of Tio Manuel,' Isabella voiced doubtfully as she walked with Terese towards the toffee-apple stand. 'We don't have any chickens,' she stated, obviously perplexed by the conversation she had just heard.

'Miss Norcroft wasn't referring to chickens of the feathered variety, poppet,' Terese remarked wryly. 'It's all to do with not believing you possess something until it's actually in your hand, and it can get very complicated.'

'Grown-ups talk very strangely sometimes,' Isabella confided thoughtfully. 'They should say what they mean.'

'Believe me, poppet—in her own way, she was!'

'Are you upset, Terese?' Isabella inquired a few moments later when there had been a silence between them.

'No, of course not,' Terese smiled a little and impulsively hugged the little girl, then said brightly, 'What would you like to see now?'

'The horses in that paddock over there,' came the quick reply. 'Don't they look splendid?'

Terese agreed that they did, and for the following ten minutes listened attentively as Isabella proceeded to give as much information as she possessed to do with horses, then they wandered slowly back to the stand, pausing to buy two sticks of candyfloss, all pink and sugar-spun.

'Two sticky children, safely returned,' Manuel teased musingly as he viewed them indulgently.

'That's what the funny lady called us,' Isabella told him, then giggled as he took a handkerchief from his pocket and wiped her mouth.

'What funny lady, *pequeña?*'

'A Miss Norcroft,' Isabella announced promptly, obediently licking her lips so that her uncle could clean away the last sticky remains of the candyfloss. 'She talked about counting chickens that were not really chickens at all, and said she was a friend of yours. But

148

I don't think she is, and afterwards Terese went very quiet and said she wasn't upset when I asked—but she was, I could tell. It's very complicated, Tio Manuel—Terese said so.'

He cast Terese a surprisingly alert glance and met the careful blandness of her expression. 'Ah, *si*,' he agreed gently, 'it does indeed sound most complicated. What else did Terese say, *chica*?'

'Something about the chickens not being chickens with feathers,' she puzzled comically. 'And me not being a duty. Is that enough, Tio Manuel?'

'You mean there is more?'

'I can't remember exactly—except Terese was angry, I think.'

Terese moved a hand impatiently and shot Manuel a look that spoke volumes. 'I'm quite able to speak for myself,' she managed mildly enough, although there was nothing mild about the determined way she tried to extricate her hand from his grasp. His grip was like steel, and short of making the kind of fuss that Isabella couldn't fail to notice, she had little option but to leave her hand where it was.

They joined Doña Luisa and Emilia at the railing to watch the semi-final of the show-jumping, and throughout that and the following final event Terese stood at Manuel's side with his arm about her shoulders as he held her possessively close. Every now and again he would look down at her with a studied intimacy that brought the swift colour flooding to her cheeks, but it was anger against him and not embarrassment that he should choose to act this way. For it was an act specifically designed for Nadine Norcroft's benefit, of that Terese was convinced, and for the remainder of the afternoon she seethed, sure that if he continued with it after

149

they left the Pony Club she wouldn't be able to contain herself a moment longer. To make matters worse, he was aware of her discomfiture and amusement lurked in the depths of his eyes all through dinner that evening. It took all her strength to appear civil, and as soon as she could decently escape she pleaded a headache and retreated upstairs to bed.

Once there she took a hot leisurely shower, then slipped between the bedcovers and determinedly switched off the bedlamp. With luck she would be asleep by the time Manuel came upstairs, and if sleep eluded her she would give a darned good pretence of being well into the land of dreams!

An hour later she was no closer to sleep and a sight angrier, for the more she went over the previous eight hours the more furiously resentful she became, and when she heard the bedroom door open and then click shut she was as tense as a tightly-coiled spring. With her eyes determinedly closed she heard him enter his dressing-room followed by the hiss of the shower in the bathroom. It wasn't a particularly quick shower, nor did he seem to be in any hurry to come to bed. Either he thought her well and truly asleep, or else he was deliberately taking his time.

For all of three minutes after he slid between the sheets she thought it was the former, then his voice, low and decidedly amused, addressed her in the dark.

'*Querida*, you are much too furious to enable an easy sleep. Besides, when you sleep you do not breathe quite so deeply or so slowly.'

At his mocking drawl she whispered in utter fury, 'Your behaviour was despicable!'

'Easy, my little cat,' he warned sardonically. 'You would have reason to complain if I had chosen to ignore

150

your verbal brush with Nadine this afternoon.'

'I'm well able to defend myself. There was no need for you to act so possessively proprietorial afterwards, or to question Isabella in my presence as if I weren't present at all!'

'That rankled—*si?*' A light chuckle escaped his throat.

'*Si—yes!*' Terese whispered vehemently, and with an angry movement she hunched her knees together and hugged them tightly against her bosom.

'*Ay-ay-ay,*' he sighed quizzically. 'You are indeed a furious ball of feminine humanity—like the kitten whose fur has just been stroked the wrong way, hmmn?'

She didn't deign to answer and a few minutes later his hand tangled in her hair, and she uttered an angry gasp of pain as he exerted pressure on the tender roots.

'If it is a fight you want, you shall have one,' he warned softly. 'But this wall of silence I will not endure.'

'You're hurting me,' she accused irrationally.

'On the contrary—I haven't begun to hurt you at all,' he answered dryly.

'Why did you have to carry the pretence so far?' she queried vexedly.

'You are sure it is pretence? To call you *niña* is indeed appropriate.'

'I'm not a child!'

'No?' His fingers soothed the warm skin at her throat before trailing down to unfasten the buttons of her pyjama jacket. 'Come, *mi mujer*—be kissed and caressed by a husband whose only crime, it seems, was to gaze at you adoringly for much of the afternoon and early evening.' There was a note of wry humour in his voice that provoked an angry retort.

'You kept looking as if you couldn't wait to make love

151

to me, Manuel Delgado. We both know why—and I'm quite sure most everyone else at the Pony Club knew why! Nadine Norcroft's particular charms seem to have a certain notoriety!'

Manuel's soft chuckle sounded deep in the darkness of the room and in one swift movement he gathered her fiercely-struggling form against him, holding her firmly as his lips sought the soft warm skin of her neck.

Terese lay passively, sure that to fight him physically would prove a fruitless and painful exercise. She began to hate her treacherous body as passivity vanished and passionate response sent her senses soaring, achingly alive. There was something infinitely sensual about the quality of his native language and it brought the tentative query to her lips.

'Will you teach me Spanish, Manuel?'

'In the middle of lovemaking you ask me to teach you Spanish?'

Terese smiled and couldn't refrain from saying, 'I dare you to repeat what you've just said in English.'

His lips trailed to the lobe of her ear, which he caught between his teeth. 'That kind of Spanish you are not yet ready for, I think, and a literal translation would lose much of the original meaning.'

'Manuel—that's a very adroit way of saying you don't intend to tell me!'

'*Si*,' he acknowledged gently. 'And when you become fluent in Spanish I will say it in Portuguese.'

'That's unfair,' she protested, and felt strangely hurt.

'Ah, *amada*,' he chided softly, 'still you do not know when I seek to tease? I promise I will tell you after Madre and Emilia have departed for Europe.' He planted a hard kiss to her mouth and effectively silenced any further protests she might have voiced.

The following few days fled swiftly in a leisurely round of shopping, and each sojourn into the city boutiques resulted in the Daimler being overloaded with variously assorted packages that contained everything from shoes to elegant dresses, lingerie and jewellery.

Having always been accustomed to spending money wisely, Terese was incredulous that Doña Luisa thought nothing of spending upwards of several hundred dollars on just one dress. It appeared Emilia had expensive tastes too, but she was far from impulsive and always knew exactly what she wanted before embarking on a shopping spree. Isabella was a delight to take with them and seemed to possess an instinct as to colour and style that was far beyond her years. It was she who persuaded Terese to purchase a clinging full-length evening gown of cream Arnel jersey with long silk fringes draped obliquely across the bodice and skirt. Doña Luisa declared it needed a long fur coat to really set it off. Nothing less than mink would do, and Terese felt faint at the thought of owning the beautiful coat that was finally chosen. A wedding gift, Doña Luisa insisted, and she refused to listen to a word Terese uttered in protest.

'I notice you wear only a wedding ring, my dear,' Doña Luisa commented towards the end of a somewhat exhausting week. It was after dinner and they were drinking coffee in the *sala*.

'I prefer a simple gold band,' Terese said quickly, then added quite truthfully, 'I'm not over-fond of jewellery.'

Doña Luisa's eyebrows rose a little and she smiled gently at her daughter-in-law. 'Emeralds have always been the traditional stone given to each Delgado bride. Manuel?'

'It is being taken care of, Madre, never fear,' Manuel smiled genially.

'No, Manuel,' Terese shook her head and her eyes sparkled determinedly as she met his quizzical expression.

'Si, Terese,' he answered mockingly. 'Madre has merely precipitated what was to have been a prospective gift.'

'I'd much rather have something else. A bracelet— even perfume,' she declared desperately.

'I imagine the craftsman responsible for designing the ring would not agree with you, *amada*,' he drawled musingly. 'It is scarcely an inexpensive bauble.'

'I should hope not!' his mother exclaimed with a light laugh.

'Really, Terese,' Emilia chastised. 'Manuel is well able to afford it. Why not gracefully accept such gifts?'

Terese saw that Doña Luisa was looking at her with gentle curiosity and she quickly forced a smile to her lips. 'Why not?' she echoed lightly, and reaching up she touched cool lips to her husband's cheek. '*Gracias*, Manuel.'

His dark eyes gleamed with devilish laughter as he stretched out an idle hand to caress her hair. 'I shall see that you do, *mi esposa*.' Deliberately he bent and kissed the lips she had laid momentarily against his cheek only seconds before. He took his time and seemed not at all embarrassed that both his mother and Emilia were witness to such a display of affection.

Somehow Terese managed to smile and converse with a semblance of normality during the next hour before they all retired upstairs to bed.

Almost as soon as Manuel closed the bedroom door behind him she turned and declared seriously, 'If you give me a betrothal ring, I'll never wear it.'

'In heaven's name, why not?'

154

'Because it means love, a whole lifetime together, and —several other things,' she paused hesitantly.

There was a lazy gleam in the dark glance he spared her, and it seemed he was choosing his words with care. 'Ah, I see you are aware of its significance.' His voice came as a slow accented drawl. 'Tell me, *querida*, what are these "several other things" you mention?'

Terese looked at him and could define little from his expression. 'You're not an easy man to understand, much of the time,' she offered pensively.

'Perhaps not.'

'It's different for you—it's always more simple for a man.'

'Precisely what is more simple, *niña*?' His slight smile was curiously gentle.

'There you go again—calling me a child,' Terese accused.

'A child constantly at war with a woman's emotions, is this not true?'

It was more true than she wanted to admit. 'I won't accept your gift of a traditional betrothal ring, Manuel.'

'I am still the "some-of-the-time-hateful" Spanish *esposo* who married you for his own devious reasons, hmmn?'

'You made it quite plain at the beginning that you needed heirs, and to beget heirs you had to observe convention by first acquiring a wife!'

'What if I were to tell you that facts can be manipulated to suit a given instance?'

'Exactly what do you mean?' she whispered, feeling way out of her depth.

'It took me all of five minutes to decide I wanted you as my wife,' Manuel said with quiet deliberation. 'The circumstances which brought about that initial con-

155

frontation I consider to have had the helping hand of the good *Dios* himself.'

'But you hated me,' she burst out incredulously.

'You aroused in me many emotions, *querida*,' he allowed musingly. 'But hate was not one of them.'

Terese looked at him and couldn't have uttered a word just then even if her life had depended upon it.

'Do you imagine I am a man who could view marriage and the begetting of children lightly?' he queried gently. 'That I would choose a wife foolishly only to discard her in divorce? *Ay-ay-ay*, you were eager to grasp at all the wrong conclusions, were you not?'

'Manuel . . .' she trailed to a halt.

'You disbelieve me?'

Slowly she shook her head. 'No,' she whispered quietly, and her thoughts were a turmoil of conflicting emotions.

'When I return from Sydney we will take a holiday— a delayed honeymoon, hmmn? Somewhere quiet in the sun—further north, I think. It has seemed a long winter, has it not?'

'Yes.' In truth it had, for so much had happened these last few months she felt she needed time to sort her muddled emotions into rational order.

'Tomorrow I shall come home for lunch, and in the afternoon we will take Isabella to Luna Park.' He smiled down at her confusion. 'Madre is a trifle exhausted, I think, and would prefer a restful day in light of our dinner engagement tomorrow evening. You have not forgotten we are to dine with Guillermo and Eva Cortez?'

Terese shook her head, unable to speak, for her throat felt constricted and she didn't trust her voice at all.

Gently he drew her to him and bent his head close

156

to hers. 'So—you will wear my betrothal emerald, *mi esposa*, accepting all it signifies?'

Slowly she turned her head so that her lips met his and her hands lifted and slid through the dark thick hair curling at the back of his neck. His mouth was warm and infinitely gentle as it moved against the trembling softness of her lips in a kiss that melted her bones. She wanted to smile and cry at the same time, and most of all she needed to tell him she cared. The words she sought wouldn't come, and her eyes ached with suppressed tears long after his passionate love-making had transported her to the heights of ecstasy.

Isabella was delighted with Luna Park, and throughout the few hours spent at the amusement centre much of her delight was infectious. Casually but warmly dressed against the cool winter temperatures, they wandered at leisure. The big dipper, the roller-coaster, the dodgems. Manuel proved his skill with the rifle and won two prizes, over with Isabella positively glowed with excitement and she reverently carried the stuffed animals for the remainder of the afternoon. There was candyfloss and hot-dogs on sticks, and all about them echoed music and the voices of the crowd.

'Tio Manuel,' Isabella begged earnestly, 'please may we go on the roller-coaster one more time? *Please!*' she implored.

'Ah *chiquita*,' Manuel shook his head laughingly, 'we must soon think of leaving. Remember we are to dine out tonight.'

'*Si*, Tio Manuel.'

Gently he ruffled the little girl's hair and smiled. 'Perhaps we have time. Come, we shall get tickets.'

'I'll watch,' Terese declared, and wrinkled her nose

expressively. 'I don't think my stomach could survive all those dips and curves again.'

'You don't mind? We won't be very long,' Isabella besought anxiously.

'Away with you!' Terese laughed. 'I'm quite able to look after myself for ten minutes or so.' She watched as Manuel purchased two tickets and stepped into the seat with the little girl held closely beside him. A smile, a wave and soon they were away, rolling almost out of sight.

It was a relatively clear day, cool, and already the air was beginning to chill as the sun dipped in the late afternoon. Terese stared sightlessly ahead, her eyes fixed on nothing in particular as she allowed herself the luxury of pensive thought. In another week Doña Luisa and Emilia would leave for Europe, and the day after their departure Manuel was due to travel to Sydney for two days. A delayed honeymoon on Queensland's Gold Coast, his gift of a traditional betrothal emerald and his shock declaration regarding their marriage required clear and rational thinking. Was it possible he loved her—was that what he meant? And her own emotions, what of them? Perhaps he was right, they needed time together alone. 'I think I love you, Manuel Delgado,' she whispered silently. 'Certainly my body loves you in a way that makes me almost ashamed—it's my heart and my head I need to be sure of, and I'm not, not yet.' Perhaps love was like wine that mellowed and matured with age.

'Terese, I waved and waved, but you didn't see me.'

She turned at the sound of Isabella's faintly reproachful voice and smiled apologetically. 'I was miles away—I'm sorry, really.'

'That's all right,' Isabella assured her generously. 'I

158

expect you were thinking about tonight and wondering which dress you will wear.'

'Something like that.' She caught hold of the little girl's hand and together they walked out from the amusement park to the car.

'It's been a wonderful afternoon,' Isabella sighed happily as Manuel manoeuvred the car among the traffic.

'And tonight you will dream of ghost trains and dodgem cars, roller-coasters and the giant spinning wheel,' he teased.

Doña Luisa listened intently to every detail imparted by her enthralled granddaughter until it was time for Maria to whisk Isabella upstairs for a bath and an early supper.

A pleasant evening with the Cortez family rounded off an extremely pleasant day, and there was a warmth evident in Manuel's eyes whenever they came to rest on Terese. Once or twice she caught his gaze, and an answering warmth kindled the glowing embers of emotion deep inside her.

The weekend passed quietly, and on Monday Terese took Isabella to the cinema to a Walt Disney matinee that brought tears and laughter to their eyes. For the remainder of the week, it was two further shopping expeditions and leisurely drives to various places of scenic interest with Santanas behind the wheel.

Inevitably the day of departure came for Doña Luisa and Emilia. A grey day with overcast skies and the threat of rain. It was Sunday and tonight Isabella would return to the convent, her fortnight's vacation at an end, and tomorrow Manuel would leave for Sydney. There was a strange sense of expectancy in the air, almost as if Terese was on the verge of discovery.

There hadn't been much opportunity for Doña Luisa and Terese to be alone—always there had been either Emilia or Isabella within earshot. But now it seemed the others had disappeared to complete unknown tasks, and there was only Doña Luisa and Terese occupying the *sala*.

'We seem to have had so little time together, you and I,' Doña Luisa began kindly. 'And who knows that we might not be interrupted within minutes.'

Terese felt her mouth curve into a generous smile. 'Isabella is bound to return soon.'

'You are very fond of the child—it is there in your eyes,' Doña Luisa said with complacency.

'She's a delightful little girl,' Terese answered with sincerity.

'And my son?'

Terese looked directly into Doña Luisa's dark discerning eyes and was suddenly bereft of words.

'There is something that puzzles me—indefinable. I make it a rule never to pry,' Doña Luisa said gently. 'Manuel has said nothing, knowing his actions alone be sufficient answer. But you, Terese . . .' she trailed to a halt, perplexed. 'I have seen you look at Manuel—there have been moments when I am convinced all is well, others when it appears you understand him not at all.'

Terese felt her throat constrict. 'Doña Luisa——'

'My dear, I think I must explain to you something that may make things a little clearer,' Doña Luisa intercepted thoughtfully. 'My own Sebastian was a very powerful man with much wealth and a ruthless sense of purpose that coloured everything he did. A good marriage was necessary, and arranged by our mutual parents, with all of the combined Spanish and Portuguese traditional conventions observed.' Her voice became slightly dry

160

and she sighed expressively. 'It was a surprisingly good marriage and bore the fruit of two sons, Vicente and, ten years later, Manuel. Both inherited the physique and vigour of their father. When my husband died, Vicente was already a young man with numerous qualifications and a zealous will to continue in his father's footsteps. He made it his life, to the exclusion of all else—his marriage was necessary only to beget the son he desired.'

She paused and slowly shook her head. 'Poor Margarita—she died not long after Isabella was born, of a broken heart, of that I am sure. Manuel was like him in looks, but thank the good *Dios*, different in character. We have always been *simpatico*, he and I. He, too, achieved scholastic honour and in business proved astute. But Vicente was the eldest son, and as such the rightful head of the Delgado Construction empire. At the age of twenty-five, Manuel inherited a substantial trust of which he uplifted a part and emigrated to Australia, determined to succeed. He has more than achieved all he set out to do—only one thing was missing, that being a wife and children.'

Doña Luisa leaned forward and her eyes softened. 'I chided him—some five years ago—over not taking a suitable girl for a wife. He reprehended me then, assuring that should ever he discover the right girl he would sweep her so completely off her feet that she would find herself married to him before she could pause to draw breath. He has waited a long time, Terese. Of course there have been women—one cannot expect there not to have been.' She made a deprecatory gesture with her hands, and her lips formed a slight moue. 'Manuel is very much a man, with physical needs only a woman can expiate. And with his wealth and virility he would

161

not have lacked for eager and willing—companions.'

I've already come face to face with one of them, Terese thought wryly. And believe me, Nadine Norcroft doesn't consider me more worrying than a rather tiresome insect she can swat out of existence the moment the right opportunity occurs.

'Whatever reason Manuel may have given for marrying you, be assured you need have no doubts, Terese. He loves you,' Doña Luisa concluded gently.

There was no time for Terese to refute or verify her mother-in-law's statement, for at that moment the door burst open and both Isabella and Emilia came into the room.

'Santanas has everything in the car,' Isabella recited obediently. 'And Tio Manuel will be only five minutes. When will you be back?' she sought of Doña Luisa, who laughed lightheartedly and opened her arms wide for the child to slip into.

'Lovely to be missed before I have left! Soon, my sweet girl—less than a year.'

'Tio Manuel said we might visit you in Madrid next Christmas—not this year, but next,' Isabella amended contentedly. 'Tio Manuel and Terese and me—and a dear little baby, if we are very lucky. Making babies takes time.'

'Indeed it does, *niña*,' her grandmother chuckled, and there was a twinkle sparkling from her dark eyes as she lifted her gaze to Terese.

'Am I interrupting something?'

Terese's startled eyes flew towards the door at the sound of that musing drawl, and she knew from the deep gleam in Manuel's eyes that he had overheard his niece's remark.

'Nothing, *mi hijo*,' his mother replied with a captivating smile.

'I begin to suspect I am poaching on an entirely feminine conversation.' His eyes took in his wife's flushed cheeks, Doña Luisa's frankly dancing eyes, Emilia's faint look of embarrassment and Isabella's complete lack of guile. 'Shall I go out and come in again?'

'Perhaps a glass of sherry would not go amiss?' Doña Luisa twinkled.

'Of course, Madre,' he assented blandly, and moved towards a tray of drinks resting on the teak cabinet.

'It has been a very pleasant vacation, Manuel,' Emilia remarked sedately. 'And most enjoyable as a guest in your home. *Gracias*.'

'My pleasure,' he acknowledged urbanely.

'I will correspond with Terese, Manuel,' his mother declared affectionately. 'Her letters will be more informative than ever yours have been.'

'Ah, *si*—all too often I have resorted to the telephone, have I not?'

'A habit I hope you will not disregard occasionally?'

His eyes gentled and he touched a hand to her cheek. 'It could never become a habit I would disregard, Madre. Now, we shall wish you safe flight, Terese and I.' He raised his glass with one hand and placed an arm about Terese's shoulder.

'For a moment she felt indescribably sad, and rather shaky and trembly inside. There were words she wanted to say to reassure Doña Luisa she would care for Manuel all the days of her life. But there was no time to share such a confidence now and it wasn't something she could say within Manuel's hearing.

Tullamarine Airport was large and modern, and once inside the departure lounge there was little more to say that had not already been said—the goodbyes, the slightly tearful *vaya con Dios*, and lastly a quick emotional embrace. Then, a silent trio, Manuel, Terese and Isabella watched the giant jet ascend out of sight.

'Such sad faces,' Manuel teased gently as he put Terese and Isabella into the car. 'If you do not smile, everyone in the restaurant will think I am some kind of devilish ogre with the power to scare you both half to death.'

'Have you planned a surprise, Tio Manuel?' Isabella brightened considerably.

'*Si*,' he acquiesced musingly. 'If I took you home, it would be only to have the both of you weeping tears into the soup. We shall eat dinner somewhere warm and where the music is both loud and cheerful.'

It was a delightful little restaurant, tucked away almost out of sight, its interior warm and brightly lit with small square tables covered with red-and-white checked cloths, and the delicious smell of Italian cooking permeated the air. There they ate and drank, and listened to the gay bouncy music until it was time to leave and deposit Isabella with Sister Mary Imelda at the convent.

'You would like to go back?'

Terese cast Manuel a startled glance in the semi-darkness of the car's interior and was unsure of his meaning.

'We have not previously gone out together without being in the company of guests. Tonight I thought we might elude formality for a few hours,' he enlightened her amiably.

'You don't have paperwork to compile in the study?'

'No, *querida*,' he mocked lightly. 'I have no intention

of closeting myself in the study tonight.'

'Thank you, Manuel,' she said evenly, unable to quell the sense of excitement that crept into her veins.

'If you continue to look at me like that, *mi esposa*,' he drawled softly, 'I will drive swiftly home and seduce you without hesitation.'

'I'd much prefer the restaurant—for a few hours,' Terese added teasingly. 'If we go home, we might argue.'

'And tonight you have no wish to clash verbal swords with me?'

She shook her head. 'Our truces never seem to last very long. Perhaps tonight we might set a record.'

'You have anything specific planned for the time I will be away?' Manuel queried as they sat together at a table not far from the one they had previously occupied with Isabella a few hours before.

'I thought I'd telephone Meg,' she suggested meditatively. 'And I'd quite like to visit the hospital—the children, not all of them get visitors.'

'I will be away two days,' he said idly. 'I hope I can get an early evening flight back Tuesday if everything is concluded in time—otherwise it will be Wednesday.'

Terese nodded absently, aware that the music had changed subtly during the past hour. It was no longer as loud or as bouncy, and definitely verged close to melancholia.

'Dance with me, Terese.'

His voice was deep and totally serious. 'Terese'—not a teasing Spanish endearment. She looked at him steadily for several seconds but could discern little from his inscrutable expression. Slowly she stood to her feet and allowed him to lead her towards the small area reserved for dancing.

His hold was possessive as they moved ever so slowly

among the mingling couples. The lighting had been switched down to match the changed mood of the music, and Terese could feel his lips against her hair. It was heaven, just sharing a mutual silence—loving, discovering—things she hadn't really sensed before. Gently she lifted her arms and caught her hands together behind his neck where the dark curling hair almost touched on the collar of his jacket. 'I love you, Manuel,' she whispered silently. 'One day soon I shall tell you just how much—but I can't here, and I'm not even sure you love me. Mothers have been known to be mistaken.'

'Come,' he bade quietly close to her ear. 'It is time we went home.'

'Yes,' she answered meekly. 'You have to leave early in the morning.'

'That was not exactly the reason I had in mind,' Manuel offered musingly.

Terese met his dark gaze and smiled a little. 'I didn't imagine that it was for a moment.'

CHAPTER NINE

DESPITE Terese's resolve to rise early and share breakfast with Manuel, she overslept and woke to find he had already left for the airport. She felt unaccountably hurt and wished for some unknown reason that he had woken her so she could have said 'safe flight', 'hurry home' and 'vaya con Dios'.

The day stretched out in front of her interminably, and after she had showered and dressed she went downstairs for breakfast. Over toast and coffee she pondered restlessly what she could do to fill in the day. Resolutely she determined to keep as busy as possible—to drift aimlessly about this great house would only constantly remind her of Manuel, and somehow she needed distraction from his image today.

A telephone call to Meg proved fruitful, and together they arranged a time and place to meet with the intention of spending the day in town.

'I'll take the Mini, Santanas,' Terese declared as she reached the foot of the stairs. 'I don't know what time I'll be back—I may even dine out tonight, and if so I'll ring Sofia.'

Santanas regarded her steadily and shook his head slightly. 'The Señor left instructions for me to drive you wherever you wish to go, *señora*. I will get the Daimler, and as your plans are indefinite I would suggest that you telephone when you are ready for me to collect you.'

'It seems so unnecessary,' she protested vexedly.

'It is the Señor's command, *señora*,' he attested mildly, as if that were sufficient an explanation.

'Very well, Santanas. Thank you,' she gave in, albeit gracefully.

Thirty minutes later she was greeting Meg with an enthusiasm the other girl found amusing.

'Terese, that's quite a greeting! What's wrong?'

'Why leap to the conclusion that something must be wrong?' Terese countered lightly.

Meg studied her intently for all of twenty seconds, then offered quietly, 'But it's not completely right— is it?'

'Margaret Cameron———' Terese began teasingly.

Meg laughed and parried quizzically, 'I know, I know —I'm impossible, and you've no intention of telling me a thing. So—what's first on today's agenda? Coffee would go down rather well, don't you think?'

'Lead the way,' Terese sparkled, adding impishly, 'I intend stocking up on lingerie today—so be warned!'

'Good, I'll stand by and give my considered opinion when required. Anything in particular?'

'Wait and see,' Terese advised promptly, and was unable to quell a smile as Meg began to chuckle.

'Something provocatively frivolous with which to tempt your gorgeous husband? I doubt he needs much tempting!'

'Actually, I thought it was time I exchanged pyjamas for something more feminine,' Terese enlightened her sedately.

Meg's blue eyes twinkled wickedly. 'My dear Terese, I don't imagine it very much matters—does it?'

'You possess an outrageous mind, Meg Cameron,' Terese admonished with mock-severity. 'I'm almost inclined not to ask you back for dinner tonight.'

'To Toorak? Oh, please do, Terese,' Meg implored. 'I'd love to come.'

'Yes, I thought you might.'

'I promise I shan't utter anything remotely audacious,' Meg vowed solemnly. 'My comments will be totally respectable and circumspect.'

'Quite un-Meg-like,' Terese observed laconically. 'An entire day with you being totally respectful might prove too much for both of us.'

It had been a nice carefree day, Terese reflected several hours later as they waited for Santanas to collect them. There was a varied assortment of parcels which they would unpack together after dinner, and Meg had readily agreed to stay overnight.

'It's a shame you have to go on duty tomorrow,' Terese murmured regretfully. 'It will probably be some time before we can spend another day together.'

'Yes,' Meg answered with an expressive sigh. 'I begin a broken shift tomorrow—which is deadly, as you well know. Then I'm rostered for night duty.'

'I think I'll come in with you in the morning. I'd like to visit some of the children—I promised that I would. And then I can finish the rest of my shopping.'

Meg nodded absently, a little in awe of the Daimler with Santanas behind the wheel. Terese silently agreed with her—it took some getting used to, and she sometimes wondered if she would ever come to blithely accept the trappings Manuel's wealth provided.

Sofia had prepared a lovely meal, with which they drank wine, and then retired to the *sala* feeling happily replete and content. With the ease of a long friendship they watched television in companionable silence for a few hours before retiring upstairs to bed. Meg had been alloted one of the guest rooms next to Isabella's suite at the other end of the corridor.

Tuesday turned out to be quite a day, one way and another, although Terese had no inkling of anything untoward as she bade Santanas goodbye outside the hospital gates. Meg had to repair quickly to the Nurses' Home to change and go on duty, and Terese stepped towards the main entrance of the large imposing brick building where she had first begun her nursing training more than five years ago. There was almost a sense of nostalgia in walking through the clean ascetic corridors. Occasionally she came across a familiar face, but it was not until she reached her own ward that she received recognition. Matron had already made her round, the doctors also, and the ward was in a state of anticipation for the lunch-trolley. Of her former young patients only six were still in the ward, although there were two who had been in only the previous year with similar injuries.

'See, I did it again, Sister,' came the cheerful cry as Terese regarded them wryly.

'I daresay your skateboard went off in one direction while you flew in the other,' she declared with a smile. 'Or was it your bicycle this time?'

'Skateboard for him, and the bike was me,' the young imp revealed with little regard for correct grammar.

'If you make a practice of visiting these walls too often they'll put your names on the bed,' Terese admonished.

'Aw, Sister!' they chorused in mock-misery, delighting in her barely-contained laughter.

'You're an impossible pair—I well remember the antics you got up to when last you were here. My sympathy is entirely with the poor nurses. You'd better have these now,' she handed each of them a bag of sweets. 'I doubt you'll remain good enough to deserve them if I leave them with Sister.'

The boys grinned and voiced their thanks, and Terese smiled as she slipped from the room. It seemed for a moment that she had never been away!

There was time for a brief chat with some of the nursing staff and a quick cup of tea with Sister, then, well aware of the complex duties for which they were responsible, she took her leave.

It was almost like old times to board a city-bound tram and ride the gently-swaying vehicle as it moved on twin steel tracks in the centre of the wide bitumen-smooth road. The huge spreading branches of the stalwart trees planted in majestic precision on both sides of the avenue stood bare and exposed to the elements, and all too soon the tram reached the Post Office on the corner of Bourke and Elizabeth Streets where Terese wished to alight.

Leisurely she wandered past the shops, pausing when anything in the window caught her attention. With nothing specific she wanted to buy apart from a few essentials, she decided to have coffee and a sandwich and found a nearby coffee lounge.

Tonight Manuel would be home, and immediately his image sprang to mind to disturb her equilibrium. The dark eyes that could gleam with warmth and light with devilish humour, or alternatively turn cold and hard like polished onyx. The depth of his voice with its sensual timbre that took on a more distinct accent whenever he became angry. A tiny involuntary shiver ran down her spine as she recalled all too vividly his lovemaking and the undoubted expertise of his touch. Such thoughts held a certain danger, for they led to speculation over the number of women he had seduced, and inevitably that brought forth an image of Nadine Norcroft.

Decidedly cross with herself for allowing her thoughts to run so treacherously amok, Terese momentarily closed her eyes in an effort to rid herself of Nadine's svelte image, and when she opened them again it seemed her vision was intent on taunting her, for standing less than three feet away was the flesh-and-blood form of none other than Nadine herself.

'Well, well, if it isn't Mrs Manuel Delgado!' the brittle voice cynically exclaimed.

Think of the devil and it will appear! Terese brooded ruminatively.

'Mind if I join you?' Nadine made it sound like a statement of intent rather than a polite query.

Terese met the open dislike in those light blue eyes and knew a war was about to be declared. Well, she wasn't born with auburn tresses for nothing! 'If I refused, would you go away?' she parried quietly.

'Not on your sweet life, darling.'

'It's to be a duel to the death at dawn, I take it?' Terese questioned with considerable calm as she watched Nadine slip into the empty chair opposite and begin stirring her coffee.

'Figuratively speaking,' Nadine agreed coolly. 'You're surprisingly quick-witted, aren't you?'

'Top of the class,' Terese acknowledged with a meaningless smile that nowhere near reached her eyes.

'Clever—but not clever enough. I mean to have Manuel, one way or another.'

'And such things as wedding rings won't stand in your way I imagine,' Terese deduced succinctly.

'That's a minor obstacle.'

'How would you regard the conception of a Delgado heir? Surely that would prove a rather more difficult obstacle to surmount?'

'You can't be pregnant?' Nadine queried with ill-concealed resentment.

'Can't I?' Terese countered lightly. 'You yourself attested to my husband's virility.'

The other woman's nostrils flared and her eyes sparked furiously alive. 'You're lying!'

'Time will tell, won't it, Nadine?'

'I don't believe a word of what you're saying,' Nadine hissed wrathfully.

Terese managed a slight shrugging movement of her shoulders. 'It's immaterial to me what you believe.'

'My God! That an unpretentious *green* upstart—such as the likes of you——'

'Quieten down, Nadine,' Terese advised bleakly. 'Re-

172

sign yourself to accept Manuel as the one who got away.'

Nadine's eyes glittered like iced diamonds as she stood to her feet. An incautiously-vicious epithet erupted from her lips at the same instant her hand flew towards Terese's face with the deadly aim of a snake.

Quick reaction was the only thing that saved Terese's cheek from those raking painted talons, and instead they drew a quadruple line of bright blood down her neck.

Nadine swept blindly from the coffee lounge as Terese fumbled for a handkerchief with which to stem the steadily-trickling flow. A concerned patron offered assistance and enlisted the help of the owner, who persuaded Terese to venture into the kitchen where the scratches were bathed and exclaimed over with much head-shaking and indistinct muttering.

'It's not that bad,' she protested.

'It's bad enough,' the owner's wife declared. 'Another millimetre and it would have opened the jugular vein. You know who did this? You want me to call the police?'

Terese voiced an instant and emphatic denial. 'If I could use your telephone?'

Santanas, bless him, came at once, and very adeptly took charge with very few words and no fuss at all. Close to home he drew the car to a halt outside a surgery, wherein it appeared mention of the name Delgado brought an immediate reaction. Terese was competently whisked in to see the doctor with little delay, and it was evident he assumed the wound to have been inflicted by a cat. It was on the tip of her tongue to add an ironical—'But not of the four-legged variety!' However, she decided against it and sat in contemplative silence, accepting the tetanus booster deemed an expedient measure, the taped dressing and the prescription for antibiotic cream.

At home Santanas had Sofia bring her a small *coñac*—'For the nerves, *señora*'—and ensconced in a comfortable armchair in the *sala*, Terese endeavoured to forget the ugly scene with Nadine by giving her attention to the television set. Sofia imparted that the Señor had telephoned and would be home this evening.

However much she tried, Terese couldn't easily dismiss the scene from her mind. The vision of Nadine's contorted embittered features kept rising in front of her eyes to mock and remind her that Nadine was part of Manuel's rakish past. Blast the woman! If she didn't keep herself occupied Terese knew she'd burst into tears. She couldn't even telephone Meg to say, 'Hi—guess what happened to me this afternoon?' No sympathetic Steve with whom to share her misery, and thoughts of Steve brought the tears welling with an ease that made her eyes ache with suppressed emotion.

Resolutely she stood to her feet and went upstairs to run a bath, determined to immerse herself in the hot scented water for all of thirty minutes before dressing for dinner.

True, she looked a little pale and her eyes seemed incredibly large when she stepped downstairs to the dining-room over an hour later to dine alone. Another two hours in which to prepare a nonchalant, even faintly humorous account for Manuel of her encounter with Nadine. Oh, dear heaven, if only she could manage it without dissolving into tears! And if he resorted to gentle mockery, she'd run far far away and *never* come back. Not ever. There was no question in her mind that she could fabricate—Santanas would disclose his part in the escapade, and the scratches on her neck were indisguisable. Her appetite was negligible to the point of being non-existent, and after the soup she shook her head at Sofia, unable to eat anything else.

In the *sala* she stared sightlessly at the television, unable to absorb a single detail, and it was probably reaction that caused her head to droop tiredly and her eyes to close.

A sudden sound from the television set brought her awake, and she uncurled her stiff limbs and pushed back the heavy curtain of hair from her face as she checked her wristwatch for the time. It was after ten o'clock! Where was Manuel? Conflicting thoughts chased willy-nilly through her head as she sped upstairs. In their room there was no evidence to show that he might have arrived home—no overnight bag in his dressing-room, his bathroom as immaculate as it had been earlier in the day. A deep churning sensation began inside her stomach as she checked his study and found it in darkness.

The conviction that he might be lying injured in a hospital, or worse, perhaps dead, turned her heart to stone. She felt cold and unutterably lonely, and as she slipped down into an armchair in the *sala* she was powerless to stop the tears that ran heedlessly down her cheeks. Oh, dear God, if she never saw him again—never felt the touch of his hands, or heard the deep timbre of his voice. Her life would become a living death. With a heartbroken cry she buried her head in her arms and sobbed unrestrainedly for what seemed an interminable time.

At the touch of a hand on her hair her eyelashes

flickered upwards, then flew open in startled surprise at the sight of the man sitting back on his heels directly in front of her.

'Manuel!' His name left her lips as a strangled inarticulate whisper.

'Si, *querida*,' he acknowledged softly, and regarded her with a dark intense expression that seemed to reveal a gamut of emotions.

Shakily she ran the edge of her tongue over her lower lip and pushed back the heavy curtain of hair that had fallen over one cheek. 'You should have arrived home ages ago,' she accused on an anguished note.

'You have been crying,' he observed quietly as he lifted a hand and traced the slight smudges beneath her eyes.

'You could have telephoned that you would be late,' Terese began irrationally. 'I didn't know what had happened to you. The plance could have crashed, or you might have been involved in a car accident—anything could have——'

'*Ay-ay-ay*,' he sighed gently. 'The possibility that your Spanish *esposo* might have fled this life caused you to shed so many tears, *querida*?'

'I've been waiting so long,' she offered pathetically. 'I thought——' she faltered, unable to continue, and she couldn't tear her eyes away from his dark unfathomable gaze.

'You imagined I was the victim of some terrible injury, *si*?'

Terese nodded numbly.

'Not that the plane developed last-minute engine trouble which resulted in a two-hour delay?'

'Why didn't you telephone?'

Manuel looked at the anguished face not far from his

own and a slight smile escaped his lips. 'But I did, *querida*. You were asleep and I instructed Santanas not to waken you.'

Terese glanced past him and fixed her eyes on a distant wall. She didn't doubt Santanas would have imparted as much as he knew of this afternoon's drama, and in any case it was a dull hope that she could keep Manuel in ignorance—soon enough he would discover the dressing on her neck for himself.

'Let me see,' Manuel bade quietly timeless seconds later as with infinite gentleness he reached out a hand and brushed aside a length of her hair to reveal the taped dressing.

Terese kept her eyes fastened on his, but beneath those thick lashes his eyes were carefully inscrutable. He released two strips of tape and carefully raised the dressing, taking time to examine the vivid weals inflicted there before fixing the tapes back into place.

'It's not as bad as it looks,' Terese offered tremulously.

The only visible sign of anger was the slight whiteness as his nostrils flared, and his eyes for one infinitesimal second lit with frightening savagery. 'You will tell me who did this to you.'

'Does it really matter?' She shrugged slightly in an attempt at nonchalance, but her eyes were treacherously luminous. 'Let's just say I failed to move quickly enough in my brush with a vicious she-cat.' Those last few words almost choked her and she transferred her gaze to the top button of his immaculate suede jacket.

'There is only one woman of my acquaintance whom I would judge capable of such a vindictive paroxysmal action,' Manuel stated dangerously, and he captured her chin and raised it until her eyes met his. 'And yes, it matters. I will not have you harmed by anyone—much less a sophisticated *cocotte* like Nadine Norcroft. For it was Nadine, was it not?' When she didn't answer he shook his head slowly from side to side. 'It will not be difficult for me to find out.'

'What will you do?' she asked seriously.

'Make it clear that any future guest lists necessitating my presence do not include Nadine,' he declared hardily.

'I think I'll go and make some coffee,' Terese suggested as she uncurled her legs and stood to her feet.

Manuel stood lithely upright and his eyes were darkly watchful as he remarked gently, 'Later, perhaps. I would like to know what you said to Nadine, Terese.'

'Oh, Manuel,' she protested. 'Isn't it enough that you know who it is?'

'No, it is not enough.'

She clasped her hands behind her back and regarded him steadily. It took quite an effort to do that, for her heart was racing and her legs suddenly felt rather shaky. There was something about his deadly sense of purpose that was disquieting. 'She said——'

'I have a remarkably clear indication of what Nadine probably said,' he interrupted cynically. 'It is what you said in reply that is of interest to me.'

'Why?' The cry was torn from her lips. 'First I am confronted by one of your—your *women* in a coffee lounge declaring her intention to have you by fair means or foul. I'm only an unpretentious *green* upstart who doesn't rate that——' she clicked her fingers together furiously, 'much by way of competition!'

'*Women, querida?* How many are there supposed to have been?'

'Oh, stop it, Manuel! Even Doña Luisa passed com-

178

ment on the necessity of women as—as——'

'Objects with whom I might satiate my insatiable desires?'

'That sounds dreadful,' she whispered shakily.

'I admit to a rakish past, but not debauchery,' he said dryly. 'My *wome*n, as you call them, have been sophisticates well aware of the rules of the game. Marriage to any one of them was never a remote possibility.'

Terese felt all the fire and anger slip away and the eyes she hastily turned away were suddenly filled with tears. She didn't want to fight him at all, and more than anything she needed to feel the comfort of his arms and the reassurance of his lips on hers to appease Nadine's vicious attack. 'It's been quite a day, Manuel,' she sighed, unconsciously forlorn. She'd spent the entire day in a state of suspended excitement and now she felt exhausted.

'You are tired, *niña*, hmmn?' Manuel drawled significantly.

'I'm *not* a child!' she declared peevishly.

His lips twitched ever so slightly. 'My apologies, *querida*.'

'Oh, stop being so—condescending!'

He stood regarding her silently for what seemed an interminable time and his face was an inscrutable mask. 'I would give anything to have prevented you being hurt,' he said seriously.

Terese just looked at him and the ache in her heart was evident in her expressive brown eyes. 'I'm partly to blame, anyway. I disregarded the possibility of violence and made a few provoking comments of my own.' Suddenly she sighed. 'You're right—I am tired.' She stood to her feet and began walking to the door, only to come to a halt as Manuel caught hold of her arm.

Gently he put out a hand and touched her hair, then bent and lightly kissed her lips. 'I'll be up shortly. *Buenas noches, amada.*'

It took all her strength not to fling herself into his arms, and for one crazy second she almost did just that, then with a strangled 'goodnight' she turned and fled from the room. By the time she reached the top of the stairs the unshed tears were a tangible ache, and moments later as she slipped into bed those tears were released in a flood she thought would never cease.

Terese overslept next morning and when she hurried quickly downstairs it was to find Manuel had already left. She sat in solitary silence at the breakfast table unable to take more than a bite or two from a slice of toast or a few sips from her coffee cup. If Sofia wondered over Terese's sad dejected face it was no doubt reasoned that the previous afternoon's events were the cause.

Restless beyond endurance, she wandered from room to room in an effort to pin her interest on something —anything that might take her mind off her state of heartbroken anxiety. Over and over again the words she had flung at him last night ran repeatedly through her brain as she switched on the television set and forced herself to watch one of the morning soap-opera programmes. Even going through a selection of LPs and playing a few tracks on the stereogram did little to ease her tortured mind, and finally she leapt to her feet and sped to the telephone in his study. She leafed through the telephone directory, then dialled the number and waited anxiously for the receptionist to answer.

'I'd like to speak to Mr Delgado, please,' she said firmly.

'I think Mr Delgado is out at the moment,' a pert feminine voice answered. 'If you'll hold the line, I'll connect you with his secretary.'

Oh, darn it, Terese silently cursed—she hadn't considered Manuel might not be in his office.

'Mr Delgado's secretary,' was briskly announced seconds later, and Terese blinked rapidly.

'Is Mr Delgado in?' she asked baldly, temporarily forgetting that Manuel's secretary was a veritable dragon who screened all his calls with efficient dedication.

'Who is calling?'

'Mrs Delgado.' It gave Terese immense satisfaction to say those words, and the effect was electric.

'I'm afraid he's not here at the moment, Mrs Delgado. I can contact Mr Delgado at the site, if it's urgent,' the secretary added informatively.

'No, don't do that,' Terese said quickly. 'It's not important. Thank you,' she added, and rang off before the girl could say anything more.

There must be something she could do to fill in the empty hours until Manuel arrived home this evening. She wanted to lose herself in hard physical work of a kind that would permit little room for contemplative thought. Anything she did in this house would probably offend Sofia and Maria; and the garden was so impeccable she doubted there was a stray weed in evidence. Quite suddenly the solution presented itself—the stud farm nestling at the foot of the Dandenong ranges. There she could bake to her heart's content, and perhaps walk in solitude. Suiting thought to action, she sought out Santanas, then Sofia, and within fifteen minutes she was seated in the Daimler.

'I will return at four o'clock, *señora*,' Santanas said

181

solicitously as he helped her out of the car. 'Adios.'

'Thank you, Santanas,' Terese smiled gratefully, and watched as the large car turned and disappeared from sight. She took the key he had given her and stepped lightly up on to the verandah. Four whole hours in which to amuse herself until Santanas returned—what a joy to be doing something constructive!

As she measured ingredients and placed trays into the oven she indulged in wistful daydreams in which she shared this house with Manuel and their children. Quite desperately she wanted the dream to become true, for there was no doubt in her mind that she loved her Spanish *esposo*. Whatever his past, his future was her future, and the thought that she might not share it was enough to bring her to an abrupt halt.

Without giving pause for thought she went to the telephone in the hall and dialled the number of his office, speaking with determined rapidity as she stated exactly who was calling—not caring as she stressed the urgency of her call. In her mind it was urgent!

'Manuel?' She didn't even wait until he answered after his secretary had put the call through.

'Terese? Something is wrong?'

His voice sounded so much deeper over the telephone and she clutched the receiver as the familiar curling sensation began deep inside her. 'No,' she began, and laughed at her own temerity. 'Manuel Delgado, I love you.'

There was a strange silence, then his voice came soft and distinctly accented. 'Amada, you certainly choose your moment!'

'I rang this morning, but you were out,' she explained quickly, adding, 'Can you—are you coming home early this evening?'

'*Si*,' he answered with an emphasis that set her nerve-ends tingling alive.

'But I'm not at home—at least, not yet.'

'Where *are* you, *querida*?'

'The stud farm,' she answered promptly. 'Santanas brought me.'

'I'll be there in two hours,' he told her, and Terese could almost sense the smile in his voice. 'Perhaps we could stay overnight?'

'Yes, but——' she paused, and almost as if he could read her mind he interrupted gently.

'Terese, *hermosa*—you won't need any clothes.'

'Oh.'

He chuckled and queried lightly, 'Just—*oh*, Terese?'

'I hope you haven't anyone sitting in your office,' she declared with mock severity. 'Heaven knows what they would make of your end of the conversation!'

'I'll ring Santanas. *Adios, amada*,' he concluded quizzically.

Terese glanced at her watch and decided to investigate the contents of the deep-freeze with the intention of preparing something appetising for dinner. She was happily content, her heart seemed to sing and there was a curiously sweet smile tugging gently at the corners of her mouth every now and again as she diced vegetables and took saucepans from their cupboard.

At the sound of the car wheels crunching on the drive outside she smoothed a hand over her hair and schooled herself to appear calm. It wasn't easy, for suddenly her heart was racing and her hands made continual nervous gestures as she waited for him to come inside. In the few seconds it took for him to walk through to the kitchen she was a mass of nerves and incapable of coherent speech.

She sensed him move to stand directly behind her and felt his fingers thread gently through the length of her hair.

'Now that I am here, can it be you are suddenly too shy to face me?' he queried musingly.

'I suppose you find me amusing?' she parried quietly as he took her shoulders and turned her round, and the eyes she raised to his were incredibly large and appealing.

'Amusing? My darling Terese, you are many things— part angel, part child, and indisputably the love of my life!' His laugh was soft and incredibly tender. 'Always I have been the ruthless savage who coerced you into marriage, have I not?'

'You're very good at pretending,' she agreed dubiously.

'And you have always been so certain it was pretence, haven't you, *mi hermosa*?'

Her silence was an eloquent acquiescence, and he gave a low groan of impatience. Gently his mouth touched her lips with a fleeting softness that sought to wipe out all the bitter misunderstanding, the hurt and the pain.

'What would you have said, *querida*,' he began reflectively, 'if only days after our marriage I had told you I loved you?' He smiled at her expression of incredulity. '*Si*, it is true. That first evening you invaded my home I found your loyalty to Steve impressive. You stood there and defied me with a fiendish temper—never once had anyone dared question the integrity of a Delgado,' he mused lightly. 'After a lifetime of willing women, you were a somewhat startling and refreshing change! You dismissed as of no consequence my family honour, my noble Spanish pride, my wealth—the very qualities my feminine companions had always considered all-important. Fate provided the opportunity

184

to make you my wife, and thereafter I courted destiny.

'*Ay-ay-ay*,' he shook his head in gentle mockery. 'You were an angel bent on wreaking revenge those first few stormy weeks of our marriage, were you not? By day a veritable bundle of fury, and by night . . . Ah, *querida*, it was the nights that kept me sane,' he chuckled deeply, and kissed her until she was breathless. 'Then I could tell you in Spanish just how much you were adored. I lived in hope for the day when you would discover a love for your Spanish *esposo*—although there were times when I despaired that your head would ever influence your heart!'

Terese looked up into those dark gleaming eyes and her lips parted in a winsome smile. 'Last night I wept because I knew if you had died never knowing how much I loved you, I would never forgive myself. Instead of flying into your arms, I berated you for being late and flew upstairs in a fine state to soak my pillow with tears at my own stupidity.'

'And today it could wait no longer, hmmn?'

Terese shook her head and couldn't prevent the tremulous quivering of her lips as she reached up to trace the crease running down his cheek to his chin. 'I love you, Manuel,' she said simply.

'Say that again,' he said softly, and turned his mouth into her palm.

'My love and my life,' she whispered as he moulded her against the lean hard length of him so that she was intensely aware of his needs. There was a sweet ecstasy in being held so possessively close to him, and her arms crept up to wind themselves around his neck as his lips sought hers in a kiss that was so incredibly gentle it brought tears to her eyes.

'I have something for you,' he smiled down at her

bemused expression as he put her at arm's length.

'I want only you,' she declared.

'So you shall, *querida*,' he teased devilishly, delighting in the swift pink that coloured her cheeks. 'But first I wish to put this in its rightful place.'

Terese's eyes widened as he drew a small jeweller's box from his pocket and sprang the catch to reveal a magnificent square-cut emerald with an intricate lovers' knot set in diamonds on a supporting shoulder at either side of the centre stone. On a gold band as wide as her wedding ring it was incredibly beautiful and the work of a master craftsman.

'With all my love,' Manuel declared solemnly as he slid the ring on to her finger, then gently he lifted her hand to his lips.

'I have nothing for you,' she faltered, and felt strangely bereft, then suddenly her eyes gleamed mischievously alive. 'Perhaps I have,' she declared with twinkling impudence. 'Only you'll have to wait for a while.'

His eyes searched hers, seeing the radiance mirrored in those expressive amber-flecked brown pools, then slowly his face creased into a smile and she marvelled how she could ever have thought him harsh and forbidding.

'How long, *querida*?'

'Give or take a day or two,' she prevaricated teasingly, 'and allowing for the strange vagaries of nature upon such occasions—seven and a half months!'

'Minx,' he mused indulgently. 'Why didn't you tell me?'

'Because it's really too soon to be sure—even to consult a doctor,' she rationalised, adding, 'I could be wrong, Manuel.'

Gently he pushed a stray lock of hair back behind her ear and traced an idle finger across the delicate contours of her face. 'We shall have to wait and see, and if not—I will enjoy having you to myself for a year or so.'

'I don't believe I'll ever argue with you again,' she said contentedly as his lips caressed her temple.

His soft chuckle was essentially incredulous as he raised his head. 'You think not?'

'Perhaps—some of the time,' she condescended bewitchingly. 'Whenever your noble Spanish pride rears its tyrannical head!'

Manuel's eyes twinkled wickedly. 'Hmmn—then you will storm upstairs in a fury while I work out my frustrations in the study?'

'Whereupon I shall use the excuse of a cup of coffee, or a glass of *coñac* as a peace-offering!'

'Ah, *si*,' he began to laugh. 'For hurling all kinds of wrathful abuse.'

'Well, really! What happens if your Spanish ire is provoked?'

'After wrestling with figures and measurements that refuse to equate, I shall probably take the stairs two at a time, seize a handful of your glorious hair, then proceed to make passionate love to you far into the night.'

'That sounds——'

'Delightful,' he concluded with a deep exultant chuckle as he bent his head to claim her lips with his own. It was some considerable time before he deigned to lift his head and allow her time to catch her breath. 'To return to things more prosaic,' he murmured quizzically, 'I rather think something is burning.'

Terese's eyes opened wide with dismay as she flew to the stove. The vegetables were beyond repair—and as for the rice——! 'Oh, Manuel!' she cried despairingly.

'Why worry? I am not in the least hungry,' he declared with amusement. 'Later we can feast on tinned soup and a *tortilla* apiece. At the moment there are more important things on my mind.'

'Such as?' she queried captivatingly, then uttered a startled yelp as he swung her high into his arms and began to stride leisurely down the hall. 'Manuel Delgado, you're quite the most——'

'Abuse—so soon?' he queried wickedly.

'—devastating man,' she concluded sweetly.

'Whom you love to distraction—*si*?'

'Until the end of my days,' she declared softly.

'And beyond,' Manuel added seriously as his mouth closed on hers.

Send for free catalog

Most of these old favorites have not been reissued since first publication. So if you read them then, you'll enjoy them again; if they're new to you, you'll have the pleasure of discovering a new series of compelling romances from past years.

Collection Editions are available only from Harlequin Reader Service. They are not sold in stores.

Clip and mail this special coupon. We will send you a catalog listing all the Collection Editions titles and authors.

Harlequin Reader Service
MPO Box 707,
Niagara Falls, N.Y. 14302

In Canada:
Stratford, Ontario
N5A 6W4

Please send me, without obligation, your free Collection Editions catalog containing 100 vintage Harlequin romance novels.

NAME _____
(please print)

ADDRESS _____

CITY _____

STATE/PROV. _____ ZIP/POSTAL CODE _____

Offer expires December 31, 1977

ROM 2084

YOU'LL L♥VE
Harlequin Magazine

for women who enjoy reading fascinating stories of exciting romance in exotic places

SUBSCRIBE NOW!

This is a colorful magazine especially designed and published for the readers of Harlequin novels.

Now you can receive your very own copy delivered right to your home every month throughout the year for only 75¢ an issue.

This colorful magazine is available only through Harlequin Reader Service, so enter your subscription now!

In every issue...

Here's what you'll find:

♥ a complete, full-length romantic novel...illustrated in color.

♥ exotic travel feature...an adventurous visit to a romantic faraway corner of the world.

♥ delightful recipes from around the world...to bring delectable new ideas to your table.

♥ reader's page...your chance to exchange news and views with other Harlequin readers.

♥ other features on a wide variety of interesting subjects.

Start enjoying your own copies of Harlequin magazine immediately by completing the subscription reservation form.